ABRAHAM LINCOLN

INTRODUCTION

OF AMERICA — This is Volume One in a series of anthology readers of the same name.

OF AMERICA embodies carefully selected, high-level inspirational and patriotic classics.

As the title suggests, the series is concerned largely with America, with the ideals, vitality and substance involved in this nation's growth. This, the editors feel, is particularly appropriate as the nation celebrates its bicentennial. Further, the editors feel that young readers have been too long denied the opportunity and encouragement to read the great literature that celebrates our American heritage. *OF AMERICA* is directed to entertain as well as to enlighten, to bring to the reader the joy of satisfaction and fulfillment, as expressed in the great literature of the past.

The student will find thought-provoking questions at the end of each major selection, along with definitions of the more difficult words used in the selection. Supplementary to the text are brief biographies of many of the authors.

OF AMERICA is primarily for classroom use, but it is as adaptable to leisurely reading as it is to careful study. The illustrations contribute to the student's visualization of subject and action in the stories.

The editors hope that every reader will derive fully the enriching substance in these diverse selections, and that the teacher will find the text to be a flexible and rewarding instrument for instruction, that will continue to inspire and enlighten the student's mind for many years to come.

Michael Murphy

ILLUSTRATED BY — BILL EUBANK ● PROJECT EDITOR — MICHAEL MURPHY

OF AMERICA

Volume One

Edited and Compiled by

Beverly Rainey

A Beka Book PUBLICATIONS
a ministry of *Pensacola Christian College*
5415 Rawson Lane, Pensacola, Florida 32503

TABLE OF CONTENTS

AN AMERICAN

To be an American is the highest honor in citizenship that can come to any man. One may become a citizen of America by birth or naturalization and yet not be a true American in spirit. To be a real American one must believe in and be loyal to those ideals which have dominated America from the beginning and made her what she is.

He must believe in the spirit of freedom as did the pioneers of colonial days, who not only demanded freedom for themselves, but were willing to grant it to others.

He must believe in the common good of the common people and be willing to forego, if necessary, certain things for himself if they injure other people of the common welfare.

He must believe in education as the privilege and duty of all. He must know the history and hero stories of America, and the sacrifices that have been made so that he may enjoy the blessings of freedom.

To be a real American, he must love America above any other country in the world and be willing to vote whenever opportunity offers, to accept public office as a public trust, and to serve the common cause in every way possible. He must honor the American flag as the symbol of his country and protect it from harm or discredit.

To be a real American, he must live in the Spirit of America, for the honor of America, and in helpful cooperation with all other Americans.

ABRAHAM LINCOLN

—Richard Henry Stoddard

This man whose homely face you look upon
Was one of Nature's masterful great men,
Born with strong arms that unfought victories won.
Direct of speech, and cunning with the pen,
Chosen for large designs, he had the art
Of winning with his humor, and he went
Straight to his mark, which was the human heart.
Wise, too, for what he could not break, he bent;
Upon his back, a more than Atlas load,
The burden of the Commonwealth was laid;
He stooped and rose up with it, though the road
Shot suddenly downwards, not a whit dismayed.
Hold, warriors, councilor, kings! All now give place
To this dead Benefactor of the Race.

ABOUT THE AUTHOR

Richard Henry Stoddard (1825-1903), the son of a sea captain, was born at Hingham, Mass. After the death of his father, he moved with his mother to New York City, where, after a short school life, he began work in an iron foundry. Every moment of his spare time was, however, devoted to a study of literature, and at the age of twenty-four he gave up his trade and began to write for a living. For over fifty years he wrote both prose and poetry and attained to high rank as a literary critic. This beautiful characterization of Lincoln is a classic.

WASHINGTON IN THE WILDERNESS

—John Esten Cooke

It is so interesting to follow Washington through the first years of his career that I will tell you of an expedition which he made at this time into the "Great Woods," as they were called, beyond the Ohio River. Both the English and the French claimed this country. It was full of English and French hunters, who traded with the Indians and it became a great point with both sides to secure the friendship of the savages.

Governor Dinwiddie of Virginia and the governor of Canada were watching each other and at last Dinwiddie made up his mind to send the French a message. This message was to the effect that the western country belonged to England, and that since the French had no right to it, they were not to build their forts on it. The person who was to carry this message was also to make friends with the Indians; and for this service Governor Dinwiddie chose young George Washington.

These things happened in the year 1753, when Washington was twenty-one years old. It was a proof of the confidence placed in him, to choose so young a man for so difficult a service. But Washington was now well known. He had not done much, but he had shown, by his life and actions, that his character was above reproach.

He set out on the very day that he received his commission from the governor. His party was waiting for him at Winchester. It was made up of three white hunters, two friendly Indians, and a Mr. Gist, who was an experienced woodsman. As the weather was very cold (the month being November), small tents were packed on horses, which were cared for by the white men; and thus equipped the party set forward and in due time reached the Monongahela River.

The point which Washington aimed for was an Indian village called Logstown, a little south of where the city of Pittsburgh now stands. As the river flowed northward, it would enable him to float the tents and baggage down in canoes; hence, some of these were obtained, and the loads were placed in charge of some of the men, while the rest of the party followed along the bank.

They at last reached the forks of the Ohio, where Pittsburgh was afterwards built. The weather was very cold, but Washington stopped long enough to look at the situation. He saw at a glance how strong it was, and that it was the very place for a fort. When they at last reached Logstown, he had a long talk with the Indian chief, trying to persuade him to have nothing to do with the French. The chief made a number of polite speeches, after the Indian fashion, but he would make no promises; he said that the French commander was at a fort near Lake Erie, and, if Washington wished, he would go with him to see that officer.

Washington accepted the offer, and, setting out with the Indians, was guided to a place called Venango. Here a cunning old French captain met them, and set plenty of drink before them. His object was to make Washington drunk, and lead him to talk freely; but the plan failed, and Washington, with his Indian guides, pushed on towards Lake Erie.

After a long, cold ride he reached the French fort, and was very kindly received. The commandant, called the Chevalier de St. Pierre, was an old man with silver-white hair, and clad in a fine uniform. When Washington handed him the letter which he had brought from Governor Dinwiddie, he received it with a polite bow, and retired to read it. Two days afterwards the answer was ready. In it the Frenchman informed the Governor of Virginia that he would send his letter to the Marquis Duquesne in Canada; but as to giving up the country, he could not and would not do so; he was ordered to hold it, and he meant to obey orders.

Washington, seeing that he could gain nothing by a longer stay, now made ready to return. The old Chevalier de St. Pierre was polite and cunning to the last. He furnished Washington with a number of canoes to carry his baggage and provisions; but he tried to persuade the Indian chief not to return with him. In this, however, he failed, and Washington with his Indian guides embarked in the canoes and began a difficult voyage down French Creek.

The creek was full of floating ice, and several times the canoes were nearly staved to pieces. Now and then the men were obliged to jump into the water and drag them over shallows; and once they had to take their canoes on their backs and carry them for a quarter of a mile before they could find open water enough to float them. When they reached Venango they parted with the Indians, and Washington resolved to push on, on foot, for Virginia. So he and his friend Gist strapped knapsacks on their backs to carry their provisions and papers, took their rifles, and pushed into the woods, leaving the rest of the men, with the horses, to come on as soon as the weather and the condition of the roads would permit.

The long and dangerous march of Washington and his single companion then began. The obstacles before them were enough to dishearten them. It was the depth of winter, and very cold. They were in the heart of the wilderness, which was covered with snow, and they could only guess at their way; and what was worse than all else, they were surrounded by hostile Indians, the friends of the French.

But they pushed forward fearlessly, and Providence watched over them. Day after day they tramped through the desolate woods, and at last they came to a place bearing the gloomy name of Murdering Town, where there was a small band of Indians. As soon as he saw these Indians, Gist, who was an old woodsman, began to suspect them. He, therefore, urged Washington not to stop, but to push on; and as one of the Indians offered himself as a guide, his offer was accepted and he was allowed to go with them.

It soon became plain that Gist was right in his suspicions. The first thing that the Indian guide did was to offer to carry Washington's gun. Washington was too wise to consent to this, and the Indian became very surly. Night was coming, and they looked about for a place to build a camp-fire; but the Indian advised them against this. There were some Ottawa Indians in the woods, he said, who would certainly come upon them and murder them; but his own cabin was near, and if they would go with him they would be safe.

This was very suspicious, and they made up their minds to be on their guard. Their wisdom in doing so was soon seen. They took no notice of the Indian's offer, and went on looking for a stream of water, near which they might encamp. The Indian guide was walking ten or twenty yards in front of them, when, just as they came to an open space where the glare of the snow lit up the darkness, the Indian turned, levelled his gun at Washington, and fired. The bullet did not strike him, and the Indian darted behind a tree. But Washington rushed upon him, and seized him before he could escape.

Gist was eager to put the guide to death; but Washington would not agree to it. He took the Indian's gun away from him, and when they soon afterwards reached a small stream, he made him build a fire for them. Gist was now very uneasy. He knew the Indians much better than Washington did, and told him that if he would not put the guide to death, they must get away from him. This was agreed to, and the Indian was told that he could go to his cabin, if he chose, for the night. As to themselves, they would camp in the woods, and join him there in the morning.

The guide was glad to get away, and was soon out of sight. Gist followed him cautiously, listening to his footsteps breaking the dry twigs in the woods. As soon as he was sure that the Indian was gone, he came back to Washington and told him that, if he valued his life, he would better get away as soon as possible, for he was sure that the guide meant to bring other Indians there to murder them.

They again set forward through the woods, and when they had gone about half a mile they built another fire. But they did not lie down to sleep; the fire was meant only to deceive the Indians. Instead of stopping there they pushed on, and traveled all that night and the next day without stopping. At last they reached the banks of the Allegheny River, a little above the present site of Pittsburgh.

There was no way to cross the river except by means of a raft; and this they began to build early on the following morning. Gist probably had a hatchet with him, as woodsmen generally carried one, and trees were cut down and tied together with grape vines. This rough raft was then dragged to the water's edge and pushed into the stream, which was at that time full of large masses of broken ice.

The situation of the two men was dangerous. The current was strong, and in spite of all they could do to force the raft across, the ice swept it down, and they could not reach the shore. While Washington was trying to steady the raft with a long pole resting on the bottom of the river, a huge cake of ice struck it, and he was thrown into the water. Few things could have been more dangerous than this. The water was freezing cold, and he no doubt had on his heavy overcoat, which hindered his movements, and came near sinking him with its own weight.

Luckily, with the help of Gist, Washington succeeded in climbing back upon the raft. They were then swept along by the current, and gave up all attempts to reach the shore where they at first intended. At length the ice drove the raft near a small island, and they managed to get on it. The raft was carried away, and disappeared among the floating pieces of ice.

They were now on a small island without shelter or fuel. The shore was still at some distance, and they had no means of reaching it; and the cold was so great that Gist had his hands and feet frozen. It was a miserable night; they lay down in their overcoats, and shivered through the dark hours, until at last day came, and they looked around.

Providence had befriended them. The floating blocks of ice had frozen together during the night, and they saw that there was a solid pathway to the shore. They reached it without trouble, and then set forward again with brave hearts toward the south. Soon their troubles were over. On the Monongahela River they reached the house of a trader whom they knew, and who received them kindly and supplied all their wants. Washington then bought a horse, and sixteen days later he was in Williamsburg, giving Governor Dinwiddie a history of his expedition.

PAUL REVERE'S RIDE

In early colonial days the only means of communication
between the widely separated colonies was by messengers riding
on horseback. It was not until 1754 that Benjamin Franklin established
the first mail route between the colonies by which mail was delivered by messenger
three times a week.

In the following poem Henry Wadsworth Longfellow, who
is America's most widely read story-teller in verse, gives an account of
how Paul Revere carried an important message from Charlestown to Lexington.

Read the poem twice, once for the story and again to catch
the many beautiful word pictures. Try to discover why the poem has
been so popular for so long a time.

PAUL REVERE'S RIDE

—Henry Wadsworth Longfellow

Listen, my children, and you shall hear
Of the midnight ride of Paul Revere,
On the eighteenth of April in Seventy-five—
Hardly a man is now alive
Who remembers that famous day and year.

He said to his friend: "If the British march
By land or sea from the town tonight,
Hang a lantern aloft in the *belfry* arch
Of the North Church tower, as a signal light—
One if by land, and two if by sea;
And I on the opposite shore will be
Ready to ride and spread the alarm
Through every Middlesex village and farm
For the country-folk to be up and to arm."
Then he said "Good night," and with muffled oar
Silently rowed to the Charlestown shore,
Just as the moon rose over the bay,
Where, swinging wide at her moorings, lay
The Somerset, British man-of-war—
A phantom ship, with each mast and spar
Across the moon, like a prison bar,
And a huge black hulk, that was magnified
By its own reflection in the tide.

Meanwhile, his friend through alley and street
Wanders and watches with eager ears,
Till in the silence around him he hears
The muster of men at the barrack door,
The sound of arms, and the tramp of feet,
And the measured tread of the *grenadiers*
Marching down to their boats on the shore.

Beneath, in the churchyard, lay the dead
In their night-encampment on the hill,
Wrapped in silence so deep and still,
That he could hear, like a sentinel's tread,
The watchful night-wind, as it went
Creeping along from tent to tent,
And seeming to whisper, "All is well!"
A moment only he feels the spell
Of the place and the hour, the secret dread
Of the lonely belfry and the dead;
For suddenly all his thoughts are bent
On a shadowy something far away,
Where the river widens to meet the bay—
A line of black, that bends and floats
On the rising tide, like a bridge of boats.

Meanwhile, impatient to mount and ride,
Booted and spurred, with a heavy stride,
On the opposite shore walked Paul Revere.
Now he patted his horse's side;
Now gazed at the landscape far and near;
Then *impetuous* stamped the earth,
And turned and tightened his saddle-girth;
But mostly he watched with eager search
The belfry-tower of the old North Church,
As it rose above the graves on the hill,
Lonely, and *spectral,* and *somber,* and still.
And lo! as he looks, on the belfry's height,
A glimmer, and then a gleam of light!
He springs to the saddle, the bridle he turns,
But lingers and gazes, till full on his sight
A second lamp in the belfry burns!

The hurry of hoofs in a village street,
A shape in the moonlight, a bulk in the dark,
And beneath from the pebbles, in passing, a spark
Struck out by a steed flying fearless and fleet—
That was all! And yet through the gloom and the light,
The fate of a nation was riding that night;
And the spark struck out by that steed, in his flight,
Kindled the land into flame with its heat.

He has left the village and mounted the steep,
And beneath him, *tranquil* and broad and deep,
Is the Mystic, meeting the ocean tides;
And under the *alders,* that skirt its edge,
Now soft on the sand, now loud on the ledge,
Is heard the tramp of the steed as he rides.

It was twelve by the village clock
When he crossed the bridge into Medford town.
He heard the crowing of the cock,
And the barking of the farmer's dog,
And felt the damp of the river-fog
That rises after the sun goes down.
It was one by the village clock
When he galloped into Lexington.
He saw the gilded weathercock
Swim in the moonlight as he passed,
And the meeting-house windows, blank and bare,
Gaze at him with a spectral glare,
As if they already stood aghast
At the bloody work they would look upon.

It was two by the village clock
When he came to the bridge in Concord town.
He heard the bleating of the flock,
And the twitter of birds among the trees
And felt the breath of the morning breeze
Blowing over the meadows brown.
And one was safe and asleep in his bed
Who at the bridge would be first to fall,
Who that day would be lying dead,
Pierced by a British musket-ball.

You know the rest. In the books you have read
How the British regulars fired and fled,
How the farmers gave them ball for ball,
From behind each fence and farmyard wall,
Chasing the redcoats down the lane;
Then crossing the fields to emerge again
Under the trees at the turn of the road,
And only pausing to fire and load.

So through the night rode Paul Revere;
And so through the night went his cry of alarm
To every Middlesex village and farm—
A cry of defiance, and not of fear,
A voice in the darkness, a knock at the door,
And a word that shall echo forevermore!
For, borne on the night-wind of the Past,
Through all our history, to the last,
In the hour of darkness and *peril* and need,
The people will waken and listen to hear
The hurrying hoof-beats of that steed,
And the midnight message of Paul Revere.

alders — a tree of the birch family
belfry — bell tower
grenadiers — members of a European regiment
impetuous — impulsive
peril —danger
somber — gloomy
spectral — ghostly
tranquil — quiet

ABOUT THE AUTHOR

Henry Wadsworth Longfellow (1807-1882), began his career as a "man of letters" when a boy by writing prose and verse for periodicals. Being gifted with foreign languages later enabled him to translate, teach or lecture on French, Spanish, Italian, and German with some success. In 1854, however, Longfellow turned from other pursuits to devote his entire attention to writing poetry. So successful was he that without a doubt Longfellow was the most famous poet of his day, and he enjoyed the greatest popularity of any American poet during his lifetime.

WHAT IT MEANS TO LOVE AMERICA

Hildegarde Hawthorne

If you were asked what was the most difficult thing to do in all this world, I don't suppose a single one of you would answer, "To love America."

Yet that is exactly what it is.

I can almost hear a loud shout, and that shout seems to be saying: "Hard to love America? Why, that's the nicest, easiest thing on earth! We just couldn't help it, let alone find it difficult."

Well, it depends. It depends on what you mean when you use the word love.

If you mean a warm sort of glow and pride, a delight in the fact that you are American and live in America, an exciting lift to your heart-strings when the band plays "The Star-Spangled Banner" and a general conviction that you had rather be an American boy or girl than any other boy or girl the world holds, then I agree with you. That is easy. It is too easy. It is so easy that you will realize, if you think about it all, that it cannot be all there is to love — not nearly all.

Soon, in a few years, you are going to have America in your keeping. According to what you are, what you do, America will be. It is you who will tomorrow be the law-makers, the governors, the congressmen, and presidents and voters. You and America will be one. If you really love her, you are going to give her the best of yourselves. And that means the hardest sort of work, the most understanding service. It means that you will not be blind to her faults. The sort of love that spoils what it loves is really a kind of hate, because it is mere selfishness. The man or woman who is contented to say that everything that is American is the best there is and needs not to be improved or changed is simply lazy or stupid or insincere. If you truly love America, you must keep her advancing; you must keep her noble.

The boy or girl who grows up thinking only of what America is going to give him or her does not love America, for loving is giving. And to love well, you must give wisely. That is why I began by saying that the hardest thing in life would be to love America. It must mean so much or it means nothing.

Let us take one item, and see what love means in regard to it.

There are the great natural beauties and resources of America — her huge forests, her superb mountains and streams and lovely lakes, her fertile fields and singing valleys. There are her living creatures — animals and birds and fishes, all part of her existence and her value.

If you mean to love America, you must, as far as your strength and power go, see that these splendid parts of her life as a country are conserved and improved. You should take the trouble to know what laws are needed to save these things when they are threatened; and they are always threatened, because a large part of America is made up of people who have no real love for the country at all, but who wish to serve themselves only. It is these people who cut down forests ruthlessly, if by doing so they can make *momentary* profit for themselves. It is these people who ruin streams and kill all the fish in them by turning factory *refuse* into the clear water, who shoot game out of season, who destroy and devastate for their own sakes and to pay or please themselves, leaving America, which they may pretend to love, to suffer. And all of us who look on idly and allow America to be thus despoiled and hurt do not love her either — not so much as our own ease, at least.

Perhaps you begin to see that loving America isn't the easiest thing in the world, after all.

I know one boy who trained himself to be a forest ranger, and who now rides the trails of the far Northwest, watching over hundreds of miles of forest and mountain. He told me long, long ago, when he was still training, that he loved America.

"I'm going to make my living, like any of the fellows," he told me; "but I'm going to make it working for America; I'm not going to make it out of her." And he laughed.

You don't need to be a forest ranger to work for America. Whether you are a lawyer or a doctor or a business man or a farmer, you can always work for America if you want to, even while you work for yourself. But each one of you should try to do something definite for this country of yours, which you love. It is your country, and yet not quite yours, for it is only held in trust. After you, come others, and if you try, you can hand it on better and finer and more beautiful than it was when you took it over.

But you can't do all this easily. You must know what America needs and how to get it. You must bring your brains and your hands and your time to her service. You will need to be interested, and you will need to interest others. But surely, if you love America, all this will be a labor of love.

I read a letter in one of the newspapers written by an American who had just come back from a trip right across the continent and up and down it. And he wrote that what struck him most was the dirt and litter spread everywhere.

The city streets and parks from coast to coast were strewn with papers and rubbish, he said. Down in the Grand Canyon, along the trails of the Yosemite, even, he saw rubbish left by traveling campers. From the car windows he saw litter, and along river banks and lake shores it met him.

"What's the matter with us?" he wanted to know. "Are we the dirtiest people in the world, or don't we care what our country looks like?"

If we do care, we are going to take hold and see that things are cleaned up and that the dirty and untidy and careless people are made to take more thought for the welfare of others and the beauty of this country that should be worth a little trouble to us all.

No nation is free that regards *license* and selfishness as freedom. True freedom is jealous of the freedom of all. The American who prefers to save himself trouble at the expense of everyone else, and who strews ugliness in the place of beauty, is not a good American; he does not love his country and is not fit for his freedom. One might as well say that a woman who kept her home dirty and messy, her children unwashed, and herself unkempt was a good housekeeper and loved her home. Laziness and untidiness are forms of selfishness, not of freedom.

There are splendid things to do for America, and you boys and girls who are now growing up to take your places at the great task of making a country will do them. You will do them, or they will not be done. You are the future. Are you really thinking of this? Are you loving America well enough to plan a little and study a little toward the time when you will be called to take hold of the job?

Is it not thrilling to know that it is you who will have to answer so many of the questions the world is asking today? Not only will you, loving our America, work for her outer robe of beauty, for the preservation of her natural resources and glories, for the cleaning of her cities and towns, but you will work for her spirit.

You cannot all be leaders, though from you must come leaders and guides. But you can each and all be true Americans. It will be you who decide whether or not America is to remain true to the great ideals that have led her in the past. No one can tell what rocks are ahead. You will have to steer, and, according to your steering, you will make harbor or go to wreck. But if you are trained, if you care, if you love, you will not fail to make harbor.

We should none of us ever forget that we are, among other things, citizens.

Young American, you think of your future, and what you will do for it, how you will prepare for it. Do not forget, too, to think of America's future, and to prepare for that. It is worth preparing for. It is a greater future than your own, more *enduring*, more important. And it will owe part of itself to you.

If you ask this boy or that boy, this girl or the other, what he or she is going to be, all sorts of answers will be given. One will be an electrical engineer, one an airplane builder, one a lawyer. This girl means to marry and have children of her own; that one wishes to paint or write or to go into business.

But all are going to be citizens. And all should think of that, too, as part of the life that is coming.

Love America. Love to swim in her shining waters, to camp in her woods and climb her trails. Love to see and know her many sides, her different climates and ways of life. Don't think of America as simply your own town or village or farm or ranch or city. Think of all of her, so various and mighty and good, stretching from to sea and gulf to lakes, and reaching on beyond, as she does. Think of her as linked to the rest of the world, as she is.

Think of her as coming from the past and going on into the future. And make up your minds that you will do something for her, something worth the love you say you have for her. Love wishes to give, to serve, to help. That only is love.

Love America. But love her wisely. Work hard to cure the faults, the mistakes under which she labors. Work to bring her closer to the ideal that is the real America. Be glad of your responsibilities toward her. Do not leave her to be ruled by a few who make it their business and profit to rule. She is your job, your country. She needs you.

Many men have loved America enough to die for her. Some have loved her well enough to give up all hope of fortune and ease for her. Some have sacrificed name and station for her. Love is the greatest, the most compelling taskmaster on earth. If you love America, you have a great job on your hands.

But there is none better. If you love her, you may not die rich, and you may have had bitter things to meet and disappointments to endure. But you will probably have been happy through it all. For love is a wonderful thing, and brings its own rewards.

momentary — that which lasts only a short time
refuse — wastes; garbage
license — misuse of freedom; disregarding laws to do as one pleases
enduring — lasting

THINKING IT THROUGH

1. Explain this statement: "The sort of love that spoils what it loves is really a kind of hate, because it is mere selfishness."
2. The author says: "The boy or girl who grows up thinking only of what America is going to give him or her does not love America, for loving is giving." What can you give that doesn't cost money?
3. Explain how you can love by giving of yourself: (a) in your home (b) at school (c) in your neighborhood (d) with your friends.
4. Explain the meaning of: "No nation is free that regards license and selfishness as freedom."
5. Tell in your own words what it means to love America.

GEORGE WASHINGTON

George P. Krapp

When we speak of George Washington, we must think of him as a hero not of the ancient but of the modern world. He was not a knight on horseback, not a St. George fighting terrible but vague dragons. He was a man who lived the ordinary life of men, attending to his duties day by day just as other men must do. He was different, however, in that he did what other men would have been glad to do but could not do. This is what made him a leader. Men saw in him what they themselves would like to be.

The character of George Washington cannot be summed up in a few brief words or phrases. His was in many ways a simple character, but the simplicity of greatness is a very different thing from the simplicity that has nothing back of it. Washington was not merely a soldier, not merely a statesman. He was both of these, but he was more. He was a good man of business, he was a successful farmer, he was a skilled surveyor and experienced woodsman, he was an affectionate head of a family, a considerate friend and neighbor, a lover of cheerful living and all manly sports, and always, whatever he was, a dignified and courteous gentleman. He was not trained for a single calling, nor did he limit himself to a single occupation. He held himself free and open to do what the occasion required.

By the common consent of historians, George Washington is counted among the few of the world's greatest leaders. For such a leader to appear, an unusual opportunity and an unusual personality must come into combination.

A great opportunity, however, will not of itself make a great leader. A great cause will not even win merely because it is good and right. To become effective a good cause must have strong leadership. It was fortunate for the cause of American independence, and for the cause of freedom in the world, that in the personality of George Washington a great leader appeared at the right time.

What made Washington great was not any single outstanding gift, but the combination of many abilities and virtues to form a lofty and well-balanced character. It was greatness of character that made Washington a leader. Men had faith in him. They knew that he was unselfish, that he loved the cause of liberty, that he would do wrong to no man, that his heart was honest and sincere.

With these virtues were combined others of a more practical kind which made men confident that Washington could carry out what he planned. He was patient and restrained, not easily discouraged, always ready to do the best that could be done with such materials as were to be had, and in his personal relations with other men, always courteous, kind, and reasonable.

The feeling which Washington aroused in the hearts of his fellow soldiers and fellow citizens was one of affectionate confidence and reverence. The American Revolutionists saw in Washington a realization of the hopes that they had for their country. As the years have passed this feeling has grown stronger. Washington remains a great leader and Americans can still think of him as an American citizen first in war, first in peace, and first in the hearts of his countrymen.

THINKING IT THROUGH

1. Why do you think Washington "is counted among the few of the world's greatest leaders"?
2. What made Washington a leader?
3. Do you think George Washington was born with noble character or did he make his character noble by diligent effort?
4. Can anyone make his own character truly noble? How?

You will hear it said many times that experience is a hard teacher.
It can also be a good teacher, as this story shows.
Benjamin Franklin was one of the wise men of his time. He realized that what we
amount to in later life is largely the result of the <u>kind of habits</u> we form when we are young.
This story is about one of the lessons he learned as a boy, and you can see
how it influenced his life. Perhaps there are lessons that you are learning today or
have already learned, which will affect your future as much as
the lesson of "the whistle" affected Franklin's life.

THE WHISTLE

Benjamin Franklin

When I was a child of seven years old, my friends, on a holiday, filled my pocket with coppers. I went directly to a shop where they sold toys for children, and being charmed with the sound of a whistle, that I met by the way in the hands of another boy, I voluntarily offered and gave all the money for one. I then came home, and went whistling all over the house, much pleased with my whistle, but disturbing all my family.

My brothers and sisters, and cousins, understanding the bargain I had made, told me I had given four times as much for it as it was worth; put me in mind what good things I might have bought with the rest of the money; and laughed at me so much for my *folly*, that I cried with *vexation*, and the *reflection* gave me more *chagrin* than the whistle gave me pleasure.

This, however, was afterward of use to me, the impression continuing on my mind; so that often, when I was tempted to buy some unnecessary thing, I said to myself, Don't give so much for the whistle; and I saved my money.

As I grew up, came into the world, and observed the actions of men, I thought I met with many, very many, who gave too much for the whistle.

When I saw another fond of popularity, constantly employing himself in political bustles, neglecting his own affairs, and ruining them by that neglect, "He pays, indeed," said I, "too much for his whistle."

If I knew a miser, who gave up every kind of comfortable living, all the pleasure of doing good to others, all the esteem of his fellow-citizens, and the joys of *benevolent* friendship, for the sake of *accumulating* wealth, "Poor man," said I, "you pay too much for your whistle."

When I met with a man of pleasure, sacrificing every *laudable* improvement of the mind, or of his fortune, to mere *corporeal* sensations, and ruining his health in their pursuit, "Mistaken man," said I, "you are providing pain for yourself, instead of pleasure; you give too much for your whistle."

If I see one fond of appearance, or fine clothes, fine houses, fine furniture, fine equipages, all above his fortune, for which he contracts debts, and ends his career in a prison, "Alas!" say I, "he has paid dear, very dear, for his whistle."

When I see a beautiful, sweet-tempered girl married to an ill-natured brute of a husband, "What a pity," say I, "that she should pay so much for a whistle!"

In short, I conceive that great part of the miseries of mankind are brought upon them by the false estimates they have made of the value of things, and by their giving too much for their whistles.

folly — foolishness
vexation — distress
reflection — realization
chagrin — pain

benevolent — good
accumulating — amassing; collecting
laudable — worthy of praise
corporeal — of the body

LEE AND LINCOLN

The lives of Robert E. Lee and Abraham Lincoln teach
us that any person, regardless of his circumstances, can make
his life honorable, useful and inspirational. It is a matter of choice.
Whether your home is one of wealth or poverty, in spite
of great disappointments or unusual hardships, you too can
make your life sublime. As you read the following selection look for the
qualities of character that made Lee and Lincoln two of the greatest men in American history.

LEE AND LINCOLN

On the twelfth of February, 1809, a boy was born in a cabin in Kentucky. He was named Abraham Lincoln.

His father, Thomas Lincoln, was an idle fellow who could neither read nor write. Sometimes he worked as a farmer, sometimes as a carpenter, but he did little as either.

When Abe was a few years old, Thomas Lincoln made up his mind to go west. He hoped to find rich land and better times.

So he loaded all his worldly goods in a wagon and made his way westward through the forest. In Indiana he stopped and built a house—if house it could be called. It was a room open on one side to the weather. It had no floor, no doors, no windows.

Here they lived a year and then Thomas Lincoln built a cabin. This had a loft in which Abe slept. But there was neither stairway nor ladder by which to mount. Abe climbed up on pegs driven in the wall, and slept on the floor on a pile of leaves.

Downstairs there was one bedstead. It was made of poles fastened on one side in a crack of the log wall. On the other side the poles rested on forked sticks driven in the earth floor. Across the poles were laid boards covered with skins, leaves, and old clothes.

Instead of chairs, in this house there were three-legged stools. There was a rough table, a few dishes, an oven, and a skillet. These were all the household goods.

When Abe was nine years old, his mother was taken ill. He and his little sister Sarah nursed her and did the housework. They hoped every day that she would grow better, but instead, she grew worse. No doctor came to see her. There was none within thirty-five miles.

One day Mrs. Lincoln called the children to the bedside. She told them she had not long to live. Laying her feeble hand on little Abe's head, she told him to be kind to his father and sister.

"Be good to each other, my children," she said. "Love your kin and your God."

A few hours later the children were motherless.

There followed a hard, sad winter. But the next year their father married again—a good, kind woman who took a mother's place. She was gentle and loving; she worked hard and made the best of things. Little Abe and Sarah were treated like her own children. Her love and care made the cabin a home.

Abe was now ten years old and could neither read nor write.

"He must go to school," said his new mother.

So he was sent to a teacher in a log cabin nearby. He studied hard and soon stood at the head of his class. He had few books, but these he read over and over. He did not own an arithmetic nor a slate. With a piece of charcoal he *ciphered* on a broad wooden shovel. When it was covered with figures, he shaved them off and used it again.

ciphered — computed arithmetic

His father thought it was a waste of time to study so much. He wished Abe to be at work helping him. And so the boy went to school "by littles."

Most of the time he worked barefoot in the field, grubbing, plowing, and mowing. No one his age could carry a heavier load nor strike a harder blow. When he came home he took a piece of cornbread in his hand and sat down to study.

So he grew to manhood, tall and strong, *awkward* and ugly. He was a queer figure with his homespun clothes and his squirrelskin cap.

Thomas Lincoln now left the Indiana farm, for which he had never paid. Carrying his household goods in an ox wagon, he went west to Illinois.

A little dog trotted near the wagon. One day it fell behind and came up after they had broken the ice and crossed a stream. It was afraid to enter the water covered with floating ice. There it stood, whining and howling on the bank.

"I'll drive back for no dog," said Thomas Lincoln. "Come on! Leave it there."

But kindhearted Abe could not bear to leave the dog in distress. He pulled off his shoes, and waded through the icy water. In his arms, he carried the dog across the stream. How it wagged its tail and yelped for joy!

In Illinois a new log cabin was built. Abe helped cut trees, hew timber, and clear away underbrush. He plowed with a team of oxen, he split rails to make a fence.

So passed the days. And now he was twenty-one, a man grown. From the school of the backwoods, he started out in the world for himself.

A VIRGINIA BOY

Let me tell you about a Virginia home, very different from the Lincoln cabin in Kentucky. This was a handsome old country house called Stratford. It was built in the shape of the letter H. On the roof were summer houses where bands played on summer evenings. Around it were broad grounds, sloping down to a beautiful river.

It was a grand old house, and when my story begins it was a happy home. Here lived General Henry Lee, called "Light Horse Harry."

His forefathers had held place and rank in England. They had come to Virginia in its early days, and in war and in peace they had taken foremost place.

"Light Horse Harry" had been a brave officer in the Revolution. He married a beautiful, gentle lady, and the home at Stratford was made glad by children. There were four sons and two daughters.

awkward — lacking ease or grace

The youngest son was Robert Edward Lee, born January 19, 1807.

When Robert was four years old, his father moved from Stratford. He was sorry to leave his home, but he wished his children to be near good schools. As soon as they were old enough, his sons were sent to the best teachers.

All did well at school, Robert best of all. He studied hard and was faithful to every task. If he had to draw on his slate a figure to be rubbed out the next minute, he did it with care.

"Whatever is worth doing at all," he thought, "is worth doing well."

His teachers praised him; his comrades loved him. In the schoolroom and on the playground he was the leader.

The first cloud on his happy childhood was the illness of his father. General Lee left home, hoping to gain health and strength. His older sons, too, were away from home, one at college, one in the navy. One of his daughters was in ill health and the other was a child.

Thus to Robert came the care of his sick mother. He nursed her, he kept house, he obeyed her every wish.

In the afternoons his friends called in vain, "Come, Robert! Let us play ball. Robert, Robert! Come and go skating."

He shook his head and answered, "I must hurry home to take mother driving. She is lonely and not well. Now that my father and brothers are away, I am the man of the house."

"How could I do without him?" said his mother. "He is both son and daughter to me."

"Robert was always good," wrote his father. He asked if his sons rode and shot well. He wished them to ride and shoot well and always to speak the truth.

All these three Robert did. Gentle and good as he was, he was no milksop. He was brave and active, first in manly sports.

The hope that the father would grow strong was all in vain. He grew worse and died far away from home. More than ever, Robert became his mother's main stay, her right hand.

It was a sad parting when he left home. But it came time to prepare for his life work, and he wished to be a soldier like his father.

So he went to West Point, a school for soldiers. There he remained four years. In all that time he never got a mark or a reproof for bad conduct. His gun was always bright, his clothes were always neat, his lessons were always learned. He did not think that mischief was "fun." He obeyed the rules and studied hard. He stood next to head in a class of nearly fifty.

At last his schooldays were over. The handsome young cadet went home with honors to his mother.

That loving mother was not to be with him long. For years she had not been strong, and now day by day she grew more feeble. Day and night Robert sat at her bedside. His hand gave all her food and medicine, and smoothed her pillow. She died blessing God for the love and care of such a son.

Now Robert Lee stood at the threshold of life. Behind him lay a long line of honored forefathers. He had gentle home training and the best schooling.

Abraham Lincoln grew up in the midst of want and ignorance. After a few months in a log school-house, he went forth to the school of backwoods life.

Do their lots seem unequal? You must know that a man, rich or poor, high or low, has to make his own way in the world. Forefathers and friends cannot do it for him. He rises or falls for himself.

Unlike as they were in birth and training, Lee and Lincoln were alike in this:—to both God had given great powers and the firm resolve to make the most of them. For both Lee and Lincoln, duty was to be the keynote of life.

HONEST ABE

As a boy Abraham Lincoln plowed and grubbed, planted corn and split rails for his father. At twenty-one he began life on his own account.

For a long time he kept on with the same homely labors. He plowed and grubbed for the farmers around. He bought his homespun clothes by splitting rails.

He loved to hear and tell jokes, but he did not idle away his leisure time. He read all the books he could get, and made speeches to rocks and trees.

One spring he went down to New Orleans with a boat-load of meat, corn, and hogs. For the first time he saw slaves bought and sold.

The Negroes in this country were not free then. They were slaves. They had been brought to America by the Dutch, and sold as slaves in both northern and southern states. But the North was too cold for them to live and work there. So they were sold and sent to the cotton and tobacco fields of the South.

In Lincoln's day there were few slaves in the North. Neither he nor his friends owned any. It did not seem right to him that men and women should be bought and sold like cattle.

He said, "If ever I get a chance to hit that thing, I'll hit it hard."

From New Orleans he went back home. For a while he kept a country store. In his spare time he studied hard to make up for his lack of schooling. One day he walked six miles to borrow a grammar. When he had five minutes to spare, he gave it to his book which he kept always at hand.

But he did not neglect his work. If he made a mistake, he did not rest until it was set right. One day a woman came in and bought some goods. He made an error of a few cents in her change. That night when he shut the store he went to return her money before he slept.

He was honest in word and deed. People liked him and called him "Honest Abe."

After a time Lincoln and a friend opened a store of their own. But Lincoln spent his time reading and studying law, and the partner spent his time drinking. No wonder they failed.

His partner died soon after and Lincoln took on himself all their debts. No one could have made him pay them, but he thought it was right to do so. The debt of a few hundred dollars was a great deal to this poor man. It took him fifteen years to pay it, but pay it he did, down to the last cent.

By cutting wood, splitting rails, and other work Lincoln managed to get bread and meat. He kept on with his study of law.

One noon a man for whom he worked found him sitting barefoot on a woodpile, a book in his hand.

"What are you reading?" asked the man.

"I'm not reading," was the answer, "I'm studying."

"Studying what?"

"Law, sir," was the reply.

The man laughed, but Lincoln kept on studying.

He worked for a while with a surveyor, and learned to measure land. He was postmaster as well as surveyor. The mail came only once a week. He carried the letters in his hat, and gave them out as he went about to measure land. What do you think of having a hat for a post-office?

The man Lincoln had not outgrown the kindheartedness of his boyhood.

One day as he was going along dressed in his best clothes, he saw a pig stuck in a mud-hole. Poor piggy was squirming and squealing with distress.

Lincoln did not wish to soil his clothes getting it out. So he passed on. But it seemed to him that the poor thing grunted, "Ugh! There, now! My last hope is gone!" So he turned back and helped it out of the mud.

Mr. Lincoln worked hard at the study of law. He thought much and talked well about public questions, too. He made people laugh at his funny stories and clever sayings. Men thought so highly of him that they sent him to help make laws for the state.

After he came home, he moved to Springfield and began to practice law. He carried with him in a saddle bag his worldly goods—a few garments and two or three law books.

Would you like to know how he looked? He was very tall, lean, and awkward. He had a sallow, wrinkled face, coarse dark hair, a large crooked nose, and beautiful eyes. His clothes were coarse and ill-fitting. In one hand he carried a carpetbag containing papers. In the other was a faded green cotton umbrella with a piece of cord tied round the middle.

But as people listened to his words, full of wit, wisdom, and common sense, no one thought of how he looked or dressed—only of what he said.

In Springfield he married Miss Mary Todd, a pretty and clever young lady. But people who knew her shook their heads and said, "Her temper is not good. She will not make a happy home."

Her husband drifted more and more into public life. Whenever a great question came up, people wished to know what he thought about it. When he was younger they had sent him to help make laws for the state. Now they sent him to Washington to help make the nation's laws.

This pleased his wife very much. She began to be proud of her husband, ugly and awkward, but clever and wise.

The time was at hand when he was to become a leader among men. In 1856, he aided in forming a new political party, called the Republican. Its main object was to prevent the spread of slavery.

Lincoln said that the United States could not remain as it was, half free and half slave. And he wished all to be free.

In May, 1860, the Republicans held a meeting to decide whom they wished for president.

"Let it be 'Honest old Abe, the rail-splitter,'" they said.

So Lincoln was elected President of the United States.

Before he started to Washington, he slipped away from the crowds who came to ask places and favors. He went to see his father's grave and to visit his stepmother, his second mother. With tears streaming down her cheeks, the good old woman gave him her blessing.

The friends of his boyhood clasped his hand. They were proud of "Honest Abe," who had risen from a barefoot boy to president of our great country.

Then Lincoln went to Washington. With him went his wife and three sons, Robert, William, and Thomas. Thomas, or "Tad," as the baby was called, was just seven.

Mr. Lincoln was a kind and loving father. He was never too busy to let the boys play in his office. They dragged books from the shelves, pulled out papers, and upset the ink. Other people frowned, but their father only laughed. They were a well-spring of joy, his one comfort in the sad, hard days that were at hand.

THE YOUNG CAPTAIN

While Abraham Lincoln was making his way in the West, in the South Robert Lee rose in his chosen calling.

When he left West Point, he was made engineer. This is the work which is given the men who stand highest in their class. Engineers, a great soldier says, are as needful to an army as sails to a ship. In peace they plan forts and direct the course of rivers and do other useful work. In war they build roads and bridges, they study the ground to be traveled over, they guide the movements of armies.

Two years after he left West Point, he married a young lady he had known and loved from boyhood. This was the gentle and beautiful Miss Mary Custis, the only child of Washington's adopted son. Her beautiful old home, Arlington, is just across the river from Washington City. Here Lee and his wife made their home.

Their slaves were well-fed and well-clothed, contented and happy. But neither Lieutenant Lee nor his father-in-law believed in owning Negroes. So both set their slaves free.

Lieutenant Lee had a happy home these first years of his married life. He had many friends and he was never known to speak ill of any one.

Dear as were home and friends, duty came first with him. And now his duty as a soldier called him far from home. He was ordered to the West to make stronger and higher the banks of the Mississippi River.

Out West he kept busy with his work and with his studies. He learned a great deal about war from books. Soon he was to learn still more from life.

Our country quarreled with Mexico and the two countries went to war. Captain Lee was sent with other soldiers to Mexico. About the time he went there to fight, Mr. Lincoln went as a law-maker to Washington.

Many stories could be told of Lee's brave deeds in Mexico.

Once he was sent to find out where the enemy was. Mile after mile he rode in their country. At last he came to what seemed an army.

"See, there are the tents white in the moonlight," said his guide. "Let us go back."

But Captain Lee said, "No," he would ride on to get fuller news. Lo! what seemed to be tents was a flock of sheep. The drovers said that the army had not yet crossed the mountains. So back galloped Captain Lee twenty miles with the news. He rested only three hours and then marched off at the head of some soldiers.

Before one battle seven officers were sent across rough, rocky country with orders to men on the other side. Six came back saying they could not cross. Only one went on. That one was Robert Lee.

He set to work with some men making a road across which to guide the soldiers. Alone, in darkness, in driving rain, he rode back to tell the general what he had done, and what he planned to do. The general said that this midnight journey was the greatest deed of the war.

There were many brave soldiers in this war. Of them all none was more loved in the camp nor more admired on the battle-field than Captain Robert Lee.

In camp and on the battle-field his thoughts were often with his wife and children at home. He wrote them long, loving letters. He told them how the bullets whistled round him in the fight. He wondered where he would put his little son, if he were there, to keep him safe.

He told them about his horses, which he loved. He had to ride them very hard, sometimes fifty or sixty miles a day. While his family was eating their Christmas dinner he lay on the ground beside his horse, watching for the enemy.

At last the war was over. Captain Lee went home with honor. How glad his wife and children were to see him!

But he did not stay in Virginia long. He was sent to take charge of the soldiers' school at West Point. Here he had the pleasure of seeing his son, Custis, stand at the head of his class.

Now Captain Lee was made Colonel. He was sent to Texas to fight against the Indians. Far as he was from home, he kept close to his wife and children by loving letters. He kept close to God, too, by a pure, noble life.

He wrote home how he spent the Fourth of July in Texas. He had just had a march of thirty miles. He made a sunshade of his blanket, raised on four sticks driven into the ground. The sun was fiery hot, the air was like a blast from a furnace, the water was salt.

But he said his love for his country and his faith in her were as strong as they could have been under better circumstances.

In his letters to his youngest daughter he asked about Tom Tita, a large yellow cat, the pet of Arlington. He told about a Texas cat which he saw dressed for company. It was snow-white, with tail and feet tipped with black. Around its neck was a chain of gold. It had holes bored in each ear and in these holes were bows of pink and blue ribbon. "Its round face set in pink and blue looked like a big owl in a full blooming ivy bush," said he.

In February, 1861, Colonel Lee was called home from Texas. Great events were at hand. For the last time he was with his family at beloved Arlington.

PRESIDENT AND GENERAL

Now came the spring of 1861. With it came war, war between the states.

The states of the North and the South had been quarreling for many years. They differed as to the taxes they should pay and the way the country should be ruled. They differed as to whether people should have slaves or not. Hot-headed people on both sides said bitter things. The more they quarreled, the angrier they became.

The Southern people were sorry to see Lincoln made President. They did not know much about him. But they knew that he was leader of a party which wished to put an end to slavery.

Some of them said, "We are only partners in this Union. Since we cannot stay together in peace, let us part. We will have a government of our own here in the South."

But Lincoln and the North behind him said, "No, the United States all make up one great country. No one can draw out when it pleases."

Lincoln said the Southern states should be made to stay in the Union. So he called for seventy-five thousand soldiers to send against them. He needed a good general to put at the head of this army. Who should it be? General Scott, who had led the army in Mexico, was too old.

Scott said, "Robert Lee is the best soldier I ever saw in the field. He will show himself the foremost captain of his time. Make him chief of the army. He will be worth fifty thousand men to you."

So President Lincoln sent and asked Lee to take charge of his army.

Lee said no. He loved the army and he loved the Union. "If the four million slaves in the South were mine," he said, "I would give them all up to keep the Union." But Virginia was his mother state. He could not fight against her.

"I must go with Virginia," he said.

He gave up his place in the United States army and took command of the Virginia troops.

For four years there was war in our land. Friend fought against friend, brother against brother. There was much hate and bitterness. But high above this, as mountains above clouds, rose two men, the greatest of all.

Lincoln said, "We are not enemies, but friends. We must be friends." He looked at both sides of the question. He said that the Southern people were just what the Northern ones would be in their places. If people in the North owned slaves, they would not wish to give them up.

He hoped some plan would be agreed on to free the slaves in time by paying for them. Now he said the fight was not to free the slaves, but to keep the Union. He loved his country and wanted it to be one great country forever.

Lee, too, never used the word "enemies" in talking about the people of the North. He spoke of them as "those people." "I never saw the day when I did not pray for them," he said.

I have told you how Lincoln looked. Would you like to have a picture of Lee? He was called the handsomest man in the army. He was tall, straight, broad-shouldered. His eyes were dark and his hair was beginning to grow white. He was neat in dress and person, and sat gracefully on his handsome horse.

During the first of the war, Lee was sent to fight in western Virginia. Then he went south to strengthen the coast against attack. There were few troops and poor guns, but he put them where they would do most good.

Then he came back to Virginia. For a little while he was with his wife and children. But they were not now, nor ever again, at beautiful Arlington. It was in the hands of the Northern soldiers. General Lee tried to comfort his wife for their loss. He told her that wherever they went they could carry in their hearts the memory of their beautiful, happy old home.

Lee took charge of the army near Richmond.

Up in the Valley of Virginia were some brave soldiers under a great general. This was Stonewall Jackson. He thought that fighting and praying were the whole duty of man. His enemies never knew when and

where he was going to strike, and strike hard. Later in the war they said they could tell by a simple rule where he would be. Where he was least wanted and least expected, he was sure to turn up.

After the first battle, the North saw that the war would not be over in a few days or weeks. Lincoln called for soldiers for three years, instead of for three months as at first. The army was put in order and well supplied. Then it marched against Richmond.

The great trouble which Lincoln had from the first was in the choice of generals. He had brave soldiers, as many as were needed. But who was the general able and wise enough to lead them? Some said this man, some said that.

Lincoln tried one general. Battles were lost and time was wasted. Then he tried another and another. His one wish was to put the right man in the right place. Do you think the war would have lasted so long if Lee had taken charge of the United States Army in 1861?

But there were good officers in the North as well as in the South. You shall hear how in the end Lincoln found and supported a great general.

Meanwhile, as I told you, the army of the North was in sight of Richmond. Some of the Southern officers thought Lee ought to retreat. But he led the soldiers forward to the masterly Seven Days' fight about

Richmond. The Northern army fell back, fighting as it went. It was full of brave soldiers. Here was American against American.

Lee marched North at the head of his army. But he lost ten thousand men, and fought a battle in which neither side could claim the victory.

A young English soldier, who afterwards became a great general, visited the Southern camp about this time. General Lee was staying in a tent because he did not wish any one to give up a house for him. Three stars on his coat collar were the only signs of his rank. His food was plain, and his table was set with tin ware. When dainty dishes were sent him, he gave them to wounded soldiers or sick prisoners.

He had no small vices, such as smoking, drinking, and chewing. No one ever accused him of great ones. In small things and great, he was loving and unselfish. He would take the least comfortable chair for himself. He would take, too, the blame for mistakes made by other generals and allow them the credit which belonged to him.

The war had been begun to keep the Union. But many people at the North wished to put an end to slavery. President Lincoln felt that it would help the cause of the Union to free the slaves. So he declared them free.

About this time Lincoln tried another general. He was called "Fighting Joe," but

General Lee soon made him run. Yet the victory was worse than a defeat for the South. Stonewall Jackson was killed, shot through mistake by his own men.

"I have lost my right arm," said General Lee.

The South now lacked men and money, food and clothing. The soldiers were overworked and underfed. They marched, they fought, they marched and fought again. But they laughed and their guns were clean and their swords were bright. General Lee said there was one time when he was never ashamed of the looks of his soldiers.—That was when they were fighting.

Again Lee marched North. He met the Union army at Gettysburg. This time there was against them an able general, as well as brave soldiers. And neither the time nor the place was what General Lee would have chosen.

He made his plans well and gave his orders: "Get the troops ready. Form line of battle. Attack."

But one officer failed in his duty. He did not go forward when he was told. The men whom he ought to have helped fell and died before the Northern guns. They did not fail "Marse Robert." How he missed his "right arm," Jackson!

Lee did not speak one word of useless blame to the man whose fault lost the battle. Back he marched with his brave men to Virginia. On the way sad news met him. He learned that his son "Rooney" was a prisoner.

A few months later President Lincoln went to Gettysburg. He did not go to fight. He went to set the place apart as a burial ground for soldiers. He made a brief beautiful speech. He said that the brave soldiers who died there had hallowed the ground. They had done their part and that well. It was for the living to do theirs—to keep "government of the people, by the people, for the people."

The war had now been going on about three years and President Lincoln at last found a general such as he wished. This was Grant, the hammer. You shall hear how he hammered at the army of Lee till he pounded it to pieces. He fought at first, and that well, in the West. Some people found fault with him, but the president said, "I can't spare this man: he fights."

So he told Grant to come East and take charge of the army.

With many brave boys in blue, well fed, well supplied, Grant started out. He made up his mind to take Richmond, if fighting and time could do it.

Against Grant, Lee led his soldiers in ragged gray. Day after day came battles. Men of the same blood fought like wild beasts in the woods. But whenever a man fell in Grant's army, another filled the gap. A man killed in Lee's army left an empty place. The South had sent even her boys and old men to fight. She had no more to give, and no money to hire troops.

In 1864 the President of the United States had to be chosen. Some people wanted Lincoln again. Some did not. About this time he saw that the army needed more men.

"Do not call for them now," said his friends. "It will make trouble and people will think all is not going well. They will not vote for you. Wait a few weeks until you are made president."

"What is the presidency worth to me if I have no country?" asked Lincoln. And he sent out the call for five hundred thousand soldiers. He loved his country more than place and power for himself.

But the people were learning to love and trust him. A second time he was chosen president. They had the right man in the right place and they wished to keep him there.

In 1860 the president's speech showed his great desire to keep off war. But war came.

Now in 1864 the end of the war was in sight. His speech this time showed his great desire to keep off bitterness and hate. He wished himself and all men to go on "with *malice* toward none, with *charity* for all, with firmness in the right as God gives us to see the right."

About the time that Lincoln was made president of the United States, Lee was given command of the army of the Confederacy.

An Irishman who came to the army was asked what he thought of the Southern soldiers.

"Oh, I never saw men fight better," he answered, "but they don't eat enough."

Poor fellows! they had little to eat, little to wear. Flour was two hundred and fifty dollars a barrel, coffee twelve dollars a pound, and tea thirty-five dollars.

One day General Lee went tired and sad to Richmond. "A cup of tea would do him good," thought a lady. She had enough tea to make one cup, only one. The polite, unselfish gentleman would not drink it if he knew this. So she filled her cup with muddy water and his with tea. As he drank the tea, she sipped the water.

Day after day, week after week, Lee worked to make small means equal great. It cost Grant thirty days and sixty thousand men to march seventy-five miles. But the time came when Lee could hold out no longer. The boys in gray fell back and the boys in blue marched into Richmond. President Lincoln and General Grant walked up and down the streets of the smoking, ruined city.

General Lee hoped to get away with his little army, and marched away to the southwest. But by mistake food was carried past them and the soldiers were left without a crust. They could not fight; they could not march.

"I would rather die a thousand deaths than surrender," said General Lee. Yet he saw that it must be done and delay would cause useless waste of brave lives. So he surrendered to General Grant.

malice — ill will
charity — good will

Grant, too, was a hero, brave and noblehearted. He had asked the president what he must do with the men who gave up.

"If I were in your place," said Lincoln, "I'd let 'em up easy, I'd let 'em up easy."

And so General Grant did. He left the soldiers their horses to work their farms. When he learned that they had only parched corn to eat, he hastened to send them food.

When General Lee spoke for the last time to his soldiers, they sobbed aloud. Tears were in his eyes, too.

"Men, we have fought the war together," he said. "I have done my best for you. My heart is too full to say more."

Then he mounted Traveler, his good gray horse, and rode away.

General Grant sent President Lincoln word that General Lee had surrendered. The war was over.

Lincoln was full of joy. How he had longed for peace and good-will, a reunited country! He said the Southern states had had no right to leave the Union and so they were still in it and had their rights as states. Gentle and great-hearted as he was, he wished to forgive and forget the past.

Had President Lincoln lived, much might have been well done that was ill done. But alas! his death was near.

On the evening of April 14, 1865, he went with his wife to the theater. An actor named Booth crept up to him, drew a pistol, and fired. The president fell, sorely wounded. Friends crowded around him; doctors were called. Too late! The wicked work was done. Lincoln was dying. It was a sad funeral train which moved west, past city after city, through state after state. A nation left work and play to mourn its dead chief.

Great as was the loss to the North, it was even greater to the South. A harder task than war was before the country. Lincoln's great heart full of justice and mercy, his iron will and common sense, would have been equal to this task. But he was dead and there was no second Lincoln. It was left to clumsy hands and bitter hearts to settle matters between the North and the South.

General Lee urged his people to be patient and to make the best of things. To a lady who spoke angrily against the North, he said gently, "Madam, do not train up your children as foes to the United States. We are one country now. Bring them up to be Americans."

General Lee was poor and homeless, but he would take no aid. At a small salary he became president of Washington College in Virginia. He helped boys to become better and wiser men. As the soldiers loved him, so did the students; a word from him would rule the wildest.

His home life was happy, troubled only by his failing health. One evening as he stood at the tea table to ask a blessing, his voice failed and he sank in a chair. He lingered a few days, wandering in thought to battlefields, and then died, October 12, 1870.

Behind his coffin was led his riderless horse. Bells tolled. Men, women, and children wept as if a member of their own home were dead. A great general, a great, good man, had passed away.

You have here the story of two of the world's great men.

One rose from a log cabin to the president's chair. He ruled the country wisely in a troubled time, and died with the laurels of peace and victory.

The other was the flower of a noble race. But the cause for which he fought was lost, and his was the thorny crown of defeat.

Both were heroes. Each did right as he saw right, and filled a great place wisely and *nobly*. Of each, Americans have cause to be proud.

nobly — with superiority of character

THINKING IT THROUGH

1. Both Lincoln and Lee felt that their duty came first. What are some instances from their lives which prove this?
2. What are some duties in your life that should come first?
3. What qualities in these two heroes do you think are inspiring?
4. How were Lee and Lincoln alike? In what ways were they different?
5. What do you feel is the greatest thought in this story? Why?

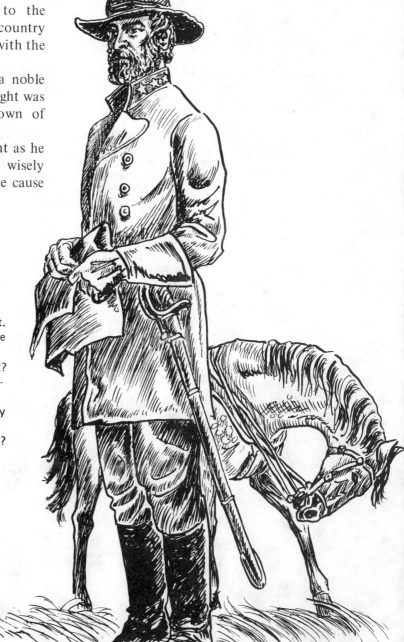

ROBERT E. LEE

OUR INHERITANCE OF FREEDOM

Author Unknown

Americans think of their country as a land of freedom, where each one has an opportunity to enter any business or profession he likes, to make as much of his life as he can, and to share in the government. It is a land of freedom. But if we are to make good use of this freedom and if we are to keep it safe for those who come after us, it will be necessary for us to stop long enough to think just what freedom means, and to learn how we came to have a free government in which we all share.

First of all, we shall need to notice that freedom is not a condition that just happens. Ever since the world began, certain strong, ambitious men, or groups of men, have tried to force their rule upon others. Sometimes these groups of men have succeeded so well that they and their descendants have held under their power millions of subjects for hundreds of years. But always there has been in the hearts of brave men a longing to throw off the rule of these oppressors. So, all over the world battles have been fought against unjust rulers, until slowly, as time went on, men won their freedom. These heroes secured freedom not only for themselves, but for their children and for those who came after them through all later times. In just this way we came to have our freedom in America. It is an inheritance, or precious gift, handed down to us by our brave forefathers who fought to win it for themselves and for us. We shall value it and preserve it better if we learn something about the men who gave us so valuable an inheritance.

Always the struggle for liberty has gone on, everywhere. But there are some champions of freedom to whom the whole world owes special gratitude. Certain heroic figures in history have played an especially important part in handing down to mankind this precious inheritance of freedom. Perhaps the most striking of all these world champions of liberty was our own George Washington. For he performed a double service in the cause of freedom: he overthrew in the American colonies the unjust rule of the English King; and by this victory he weakened the King's despotic power over his own subjects in England. Thus Washington made it possible for liberty-loving Englishmen gradually to gain a larger share in their own government.

The struggle for freedom all over the world is not yet ended. Millions of people are still ruled by governments that oppress them. We, free citizens of fortunate America, owe a duty to all mankind. This duty is to value our freedom so highly that we will make free government more and more successful in our country; more and more a model that all other nations will gladly follow. Only in this way can we show that we are worthy of the sacrifices made for us by the brave men of long ago who fought that we might have this precious inheritance of freedom.

THINKING IT THROUGH

1. The author says that our freedom is an inheritance. What does he mean?
2. How did we come to have freedom in our country?
3. What duty do American citizens owe to all mankind?
4. What can you do now to keep our country's freedom for those who come after you?

These letters are especially valuable because they give us a view of
President Lincoln's inner thoughts.
The first shows his deep desire for a united country;
the second reveals his tender, compassionate sympathy for a
mother's deep grief and immeasurable loss.

ABRAHAM LINCOLN TO HORACE GREELEY

August 22, 1862 (Extracts)

I would save the Union. I would save it the shortest way under the Constitution. The sooner the national authority can be restored, the nearer the Union will be "the Union as it was." If there be those who would not save the Union unless they could at the same time save slavery, I do not agree with them . . . My paramount object in this struggle is to save the Union, and is not either to save or to destroy slavery. If I could save the Union without freeing any slave, I would do it; and if I could save it by freeing some and leaving others alone, I would do that. What I do about slavery and the colored race, I do because I believe it helps to save the Union; and what I forbear, I forbear because I do not believe it would save the Union. I shall do less whenever I shall believe what I am doing hurts the cause, and I shall do more whenever I shall believe doing more will help the cause. I shall try to correct errors when shown to be errors, and I shall adopt new views as fast as they shall appear to be true views.

ABRAHAM LINCOLN TO MRS. BIXBY

November 21, 1864

Dear Madam:

I have been shown in the files of the War Department a statement of the Adjutant General of Massachusetts that you are the mother of five sons who have died gloriously on the field of battle. I feel how weak and fruitless must be any words of mine which should attempt to beguile you from the grief of a loss so overwhelming. But I can not refrain from tendering to you the consolation that may be found in the thanks of the republic they died to save. I pray that our Heavenly Father may assuage the anguish of your bereavement, and leave you only the cherished memory of the loved and lost, and the solemn pride that must be yours to have laid so costly a sacrifice upon the altar of freedom.

Yours very sincerely and respectfully,

Abraham Lincoln

This letter, in Lincoln's handwriting, hangs in a frame on the walls of Brasenose College, Oxford University, England, as a model of the purest English.

When Abraham Lincoln was a young man, he ran for the legislature in Illinois and was badly swamped.

He next entered business, failed, spent seventeen years of his life paying up the debts of a worthless partner.

He was in love with a beautiful young woman to whom he became engaged—then she died.

Entering politics again, he ran for Congress and again was badly defeated.

He then tried to get an appointment to the United States Land Office, but he failed.

He became a candidate for the U.S. Senate, and was badly defeated.

In 1856 he became a candidate for the Vice-Presidency and was again defeated.

In 1858 he was defeated by Douglas.

One failure after another—bad failures—great setbacks. In the face of all this he eventually became one of the country's greatest men, if not the greatest.

When you think of a series of setbacks like this, doesn't it make you feel kind of small to become discouraged, just because you think you are having a hard time in life?

SUCCESS

—Frank Parsons

Lincoln's message to you is that no matter how poor you may be, nor how many disadvantages you may labor under from lack of education, if you will study yourself carefully, find out what service you are best adapted to, prepare yourself for the field of work in which your best abilities and enthusiasms will have full play, persevere till you find an opening in that field, and earnestly strive to do the best work you are capable of, you will have every reason to expect success. The world is hungry for the efficiency that is born of adaptation, thorough preparation and enthusiastic devotion; and it pays high prices for such service, not only in money, but in social position and public regard.

*True heroism often springs from unexpected sources in times of crisis.
As you read this heroic event, picture the youth in your mind. What emotions,
what strength of character motivated him to action?*

NOT FOR MONEY,
BUT FOR THE FLAG

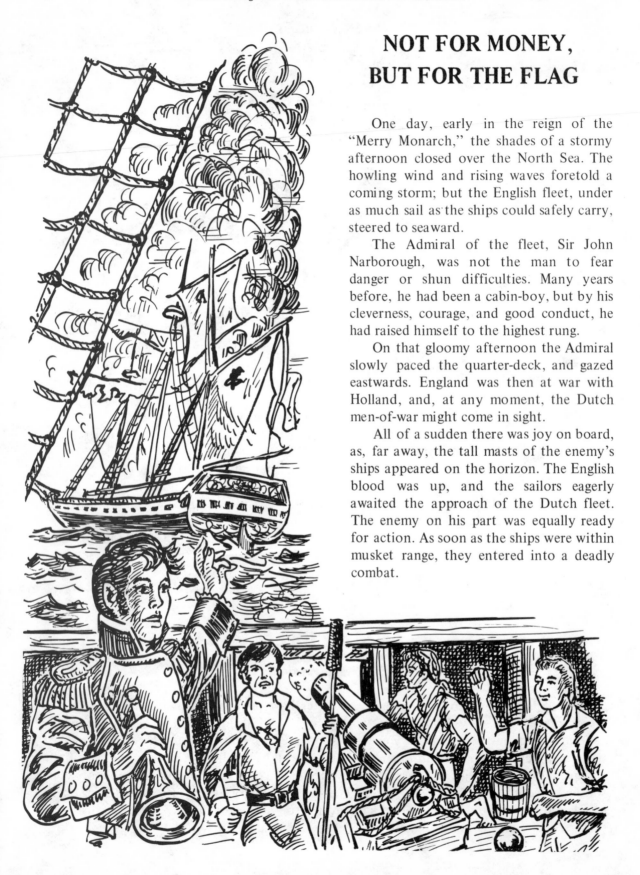

One day, early in the reign of the "Merry Monarch," the shades of a stormy afternoon closed over the North Sea. The howling wind and rising waves foretold a coming storm; but the English fleet, under as much sail as the ships could safely carry, steered to seaward.

The Admiral of the fleet, Sir John Narborough, was not the man to fear danger or shun difficulties. Many years before, he had been a cabin-boy, but by his cleverness, courage, and good conduct, he had raised himself to the highest rung.

On that gloomy afternoon the Admiral slowly paced the quarter-deck, and gazed eastwards. England was then at war with Holland, and, at any moment, the Dutch men-of-war might come in sight.

All of a sudden there was joy on board, as, far away, the tall masts of the enemy's ships appeared on the horizon. The English blood was up, and the sailors eagerly awaited the approach of the Dutch fleet. The enemy on his part was equally ready for action. As soon as the ships were within musket range, they entered into a deadly combat.

During the fierce struggle that followed, the English flagship was surrounded by the enemy; several of her guns were disabled, her masts were shot away, and her decks covered with dead and dying.

Those on board could tell that, on the whole, the English were getting the best of the fight, but they feared that help from other ships would come too late to save the flagship. The Admiral wished to get help from another quarter, but he could get no word beyond the circle of ships which enclosed him, as no signal could be seen on account of the blinding smoke.

Not knowing what else to do, Sir John wrote a note, and offered fifty guineas to the man who would deliver the message. The sailors knew that death probably awaited him who attempted such a task, but at once many offered. Among the number was the cabin-boy, whose childish voice was heard above the rest.

"Let me go, your honor," said he. "Let me go."

As he spoke, he stepped forward and saluted the Admiral, then pleaded so hard that at last the task was given to him.

"Off with you," said Sir John, "and may God keep you safe."

The boy placed the message in his mouth; then there was a plunge, and he was gone. The billows raged, and the shot fell thick around the boy, while those on board strained their eyes to catch the first sign that he had passed the enemy's line and accomplished his mission. Soon the mighty English ships bore down upon the Dutch vessels, and the flag of England once more ruled the waves.

It was a proud moment for the youthful hero when he stood on deck surrounded by the crew, who had been called together to do him honor. The Admiral advanced and handed him a purse of gold; but, to the surprise of all, the poor lad indignantly refused the reward.

"I did not do the job for money," said he, "I did it for sake of the flag; and if you are satisfied, that is all I want."

Sailors can bravely face death, and remain quite cool in the hour of danger, but even the presence of the Admiral was not enough to keep order, and a deafening cheer arose from the crew.

"God bless you, my boy," said Sir John. And the sailors knew by the Admiral's cheery tones and smiling face that their little breaking of rules had met with his approval.

THINKING IT THROUGH

1. What did the cabin boy value above money?
2. Do you think he had his values in the right order?
3. The crew showed that they respected the boy. Does this indicate that respect is earned by a person's conduct in life rather than by one's material or physical possessions?

Paul Revere was a man ready to do any service for his country. Today we usually
remember him for his frantic ride to warn farmers along the way to
Lexington that British troops were coming.
He did much more. As you read about this great American,
ask yourself, "Am I doing all I can for my country?"

PAUL REVERE

Paul Revere really lived, and his "midnight ride" actually took place. Longfellow obtained the facts, which furnished the inspiration for his famous poem, from a letter which Paul Revere wrote about twenty-two years after the events it describes. This letter was based on a deposition which Revere made shortly after the ride.

Paul Revere was, in fact, one of the most versatile men of his generation: patriot, politician and soldier, goldsmith and silversmith, artist and engraver, mechanic and inventor, bell founder, industrial pioneer, and contributor to the efficiency of the American navy and merchant marine. Like most American patriots of 1776, he could do many things besides talk and fight.

Paul Revere was the son of a French Huguenot, Apollos Rivoire, who emigrated from Guernsey to Boston early in the eighteenth century. Born in Boston on December 21, 1734, Paul learned his father's trade of goldsmith and silversmith, and eventually inherited his business. As a designer and maker of silverware, Paul Revere became one of our greatest colonial craftsmen. Teapots, sugar bowls, cream pitchers, spoons, and other articles with the magic name "Revere" stamped upon them, are now valued as much for their artistic merit as for their historic associations.

Paul had several profitable side lines as well; among them, dentistry. After the Battle of Bunker Hill he identified the body of Joseph Warren by a false tooth he had inserted in the patriot leader's jaw.

In the French and Indian War, Paul served as second lieutenant of artillery. Shortly after, he married, and in 1770, purchased the house on North Square, Boston, which, carefully restored by the Paul Revere Memorial Association, is now the oldest existing dwelling, and one of the most interesting relics of historic Boston.

At the time of the Stamp Act, Paul became an ardent patriot, and a member of the Sons of Liberty. His particular contribution to the cause was the engraving on copper of political caricatures, portraits of patriots, and the like. The most famous of his engravings is that of the Boston Massacre of 1770. He was a leader among the mechanics of Boston, who were the bone and sinew of the patriot party.

Paul Revere was accustomed to pack his finished work in saddle-bags, and deliver it himself, on horseback, to his country customers. Thus he became a skillful rider, and a good judge of horseflesh. So, when the Boston patriot committee began sending secret letters to its friends in other patriotic centers, Paul Revere was employed as a messenger. After the Boston Tea Party, he was chosen to convey the news to the New York Sons of Liberty. In May, 1774, he carried the news of the Boston Port Act to Philadelphia, arriving in the fast time of six days. On the way, he scattered printed copies of the hated act, and it was this news that produced the first Continental Congress.

In the meantime, the Massachusetts patriots had set up a government of their own, and were collecting, at Concord, arms and munitions for the defense of colonial liberty.

Revere's next public service was to engrave and print the first paper money issued by the revolutionary government of Massachusetts. In November, 1775, the Provincial Congress sent him to Philadelphia to study powder-making. A single inspection of one factory sufficed him to build a state powder mill at Canton, Massachusetts, and direct how the work should be done.

After the evacuation of Boston, he was commissioned lieutenant colonel of a regiment of militia artillery, which was stationed at the Castle, for the defense of Boston Harbor. He took part in the fruitless campaigns against Newport, 1778, and Penobscot, 1779. He also owned shares in at least one privateer, the Speedwell.

At the close of the war, Revere resumed his trade of silversmith, which he carried on in connection with a general hardware business. In 1792, he opened a bell and cannon foundry, in the north end of Boston. He was one of the earliest bell casters in America, and one of the most successful in the difficult art of producing a sweet tone. Over seventy-five of the bells made by him and his son are still in use today, in New England churches and town halls.

At his new foundry, Revere spent much time and energy in finding out how to refine copper for industrial purposes. Succeeding, as usual, he obtained the government contract for the brass and copper work on the frigate Constitution, and cast her ship's bell, which was shot away in the fight with the Guerriere.

In 1801, Paul Revere was a dignified, white-haired gentleman of sixty-six years. But instead of retiring, he purchased the old powder-mill at Canton, fifteen miles out of Boston, and made it into a copper-rolling mill. At that time, all the sheet copper for protecting ships' bottoms from worms and barnacles was imported from England. Obtaining a loan from the Navy Department for the purchase of machinery and materials, Revere was able to supplant the imported article. He coppered the State House dome in 1802, and recoppered the bottom of the Constitution in 1803, just before the war with Tripoli. He furnished the copper-sheets for some of Fulton's first steamboat boilers. The copper works at Canton remained in the possession of his descendants until 1900.

On divers occasions, Revere was elected to town offices. He was chairman of the first Boston Board of Health, in 1801. He died at his home in Boston on May 10, 1818, aged eighty-three.

Paul Revere was a noble patriot and a useful citizen. Let us remember him, not merely as the hero of a romantic incident, but as the inventor and organizer who placed his ability at the service of his country; the genius who was never too busy to take part in civic affairs, and the artist who permanently enriched his community with beautiful and melodious objects of common use.

– From the "Old South Leaflet"

THINKING IT THROUGH

1. The author describes Paul Revere as a "noble patriot and a useful citizen." Explain the meaning of "noble" and "useful."
2. Why was Paul Revere's midnight ride important?
3. If you didn't know anything else about Paul Revere except his ride, what could you say about him?

WORK LOYALLY

—Author Unknown

Just where you stand in the conflict,
    There is your place!
Just where you think you are useless
    Hide not your face!
God placed you there for a purpose,
    Whate'er it be;
Think He has chosen you for it—
    Work loyally.

Gird on your armor! Be faithful
    At toil or rest,
Whiche'er it be, never doubting
    God's way is best.
Out in the fight, or on picket
    Stand firm and true;
This is the work which your Master
    Gives you to do.

The oriental philosophers say, "What I gave, I held; what I spent, I had; what I kept I lost."

ROBINSON CRUSOE
Daniel Defoe

HOW I WENT TO SEA
AND WAS SHIPWRECKED

I was born at York, in England, on the First of March, 1632. From the time when I was quite a young child I had felt a great wish to spend my life at sea, and as I grew, so did this taste grow more and more strong; till at last on September 1st, 1651, I ran away from my school and home, and found my way on foot to Hull, where I soon got a place on board a ship.

Never any young adventurer's *misfortunes* began sooner or continued longer than mine, for when we were far out at sea, some Turks in a small ship came on our track in full chase. After a long *pursuit* our vessel was captured and all on board were taken as slaves.

The chief of the Turks took me as his prize to a port which was held by the Moors. There I remained in slavery for several years, and bitterly did I *repent* my rash act in leaving my good parents in England.

At length I found an opportunity to escape to a vessel that was passing by and was kindly received by the captain, who proved to be an English sailor bound on a voyage of trade.

I had not been aboard more than twelve days, when a high wind took us off we knew not where. All at once there was a cry of "Land!" and the ship struck on a bank of sand, in which she sank so deep that we could not get her off. At last we found that we must make up our minds to leave her, and get to shore as well as we could. There had been a boat at her stern, but we found that it had been torn off by the force of the waves. One small boat was still left on the ship's side, so we got in it.

There we were all of us on the wild sea. The heart of each now grew faint, our cheeks were pale, and our eyes were dim, for there was but one hope, and that was to find some bay, and go get in the lee of the land.

The sea grew more and more rough, and its white foam would curl and boil till at last the waves, in their wild sport, burst on the boat's side, and we were all thrown out.

I could swim well, but the force of the waves made me lose my breath too much to do so. At length one large wave took me to the shore, and left me high and dry, though half dead with fear. I got on my feet and made the best of my way for the land; but just then the curve of a huge wave rose up as high as a hill, and this I had no strength to keep from, so it took me back to the sea. I did my best to float on top, and held my breath to do so. The next wave was quite as high, and shut me up in its bulk. I held my hands down tight to my sides, and then my head shot out at the top

I felt so wrapt in joy, that all I could do was to walk up and down the coast, now lift up my hands, now fold them on my breast and thank God for all that He had done for me, when the rest of the men were lost. All lost but I, and I was safe! I now cast my eyes round me, to find out what kind of place it was that I had been thus thrown in, like a bird in a storm. Then all the glee I felt at first left me; for I was wet and cold, and had no dry clothes to put on, no food to eat, and not a friend to help me.

I feared that there might be wild beasts here, and I had no gun to shoot them with, or to keep me from their jaws. I had but a knife and a pipe.

It now grew dark; and where was I to go for the night? I thought the top of some high tree would be a good place to keep me out of harm's way; and that there I might sit and think of death, for, as yet, I had no hopes of life. Well, I went to my tree, and made a kind of nest to sleep in. Then I cut a stick to keep off the beasts of prey, in case any should come, and fell to sleep just as if the branch I lay on had been a bed of down.

When I woke up it was broad day; the sky too was clear and the sea calm. But I saw from the top of the tree that in the night the ship had left the bank of sand, and lay but a mile from me. I soon threw off my clothes, took to the sea, and swam up to the wreck. But how was I to get on deck? I had gone twice around the ship, when a piece of rope caught my eye, which hung down from her side so low that at first the waves hit it. By the help of this rope I got on board.

HOW I MADE AND USED A RAFT

I found that there was a bulge in the ship, and that she had sprung a leak. You may be sure that my first thought was to look around for some food, and I soon made my way to the bin for there was no time to lose. What I stood most in need of was a boat to take the goods to shore. But it was vain to wish for that which could not be had; and as there were some spare yards

of the waves. This gave me breath, and soon my feet felt the ground.

I stood quite still for a short time, to let the sea run back from me, and then I set off with all my might to the shore, but yet the waves caught me, and twice more did they take me back, and twice more land me on the shore. I thought the last wave would have been the death of me, for it drove me on a piece of rock, and with such force as to leave me in a kind of *swoon.* I soon regained my senses and got up to the cliffs close to the shore, where I found some grass, out of the reach of the sea. There I sat down, safe on land at last.

in the ship, two or three large planks, and a mast or two, I fell to work with these to make a raft.

I put four *spars* side by side, and laid short bits of plank on them, cross-ways, to make my raft strong. Though these planks would bear my own weight, they were too slight to bear much of my freight. So I took a saw which was on board, and cut a mast in three lengths, and these gave great strength to the raft. I found some bread and rice, a Dutch cheese, and some dry goat's flesh.

My next task was to screen my goods from the spray of the sea; and this did not take long, for there were three large chests on board which held all, and these I put on the raft.

"See, here is a prize!" said I, out loud (though there was none to hear me); "now I shall not starve." For I found four large guns. But how was my raft to be got to land? I had no sail, no oars; and a gust of wind would make all my store slide off. Yet there were three things which I was glad of--a calm sea, a tide which set in to the shore, and slight breeze to blow me there.

I had the good luck to find some oars in a part of the ship in which I had made no search till now. With these I put to sea, and for half a mile my raft went well; but soon I found it driven to one side. At length I saw a creek, up which, with some toil, I took my raft.

I saw that there were birds on the *isle,* and I shot one of them. Mine must have been the first gun that had been heard there since the world was made; for, at the sound of it, whole flocks of birds flew up, with loud cries, from all parts of the wood. The shape of the beak of the one I shot was like that of a hawk, but the claws were not so large.

I now went back to my raft to land my stores and this took up the rest of the day.

What to do at night I knew not, nor where to find a safe place to land my stores on. I did not like to lie down on the ground, for fear of beasts of prey, as well as snakes, but there was no cause for these fears, as I have since found. I put the chests

and boards round me as well as I could and made a kind of hut for the night.

As there was still a great store of things left in the ship which would be of use to me, I thought that I ought to bring them to land at once; for I knew that the first storm would break up the ship. So I went on board, and took good care this time not to load my raft too much.

The first thing I sought for was the tool chest; and in it were some bags of nails, spikes, saws, knives, and such things; but best of all, I found a stone to grind my tools on. There were two or three flasks, some large bags of shot, and a roll of lead; but this last I had not the strength to hoist up to the ship's side, so as to get it on my raft. There were some spare sails too, which I brought to shore.

Now that I had two freights of goods on hand, I made a tent with the ship's sails, to stow them in, and cut the poles for it from the wood. I now took all the things out of the casks and chests, and put the casks in piles round the tent, to give it strength; and when this was done, I shut up the door with the boards, spread one of the beds, which I had brought from the ship, on the ground, laid two guns close to my head, and went to bed for the first time. I slept all night, for I was much in need of rest.

The next day I was sad and sick at heart, for I felt how dull it was to be thus cut off from all the rest of the world! I had no great wish for work: but there was too much to be done for me to dwell long on my sad lot. Each day, as it came, I went off to the wreck to *fetch* more things; and I brought back as much as the raft would hold.

The last time I went to the wreck, the wind blew so hard that I made up my mind to go on board next time at low tide. I found some tea and some gold coin; but as to the gold, it made me laugh to look at it. "O drug!" said I, "thou art of no use to me! I care not to save thee. Stay where thou art till the ship goes down; then go thou with it!"

Still, I thought I might just as well take it; so I put it in a piece of the sail, and threw it on deck that I might place it on the raft. By-and-by the wind blew from the shore, so I had to hurry back with all speed; for I knew that at the turn of the tide I should find it hard work to get to land at all. But in spite of the high wind, I came to my home all safe. At dawn I put my head out, and cast my eyes on the sea, when lo! no ship was there!

This great change in the face of things, and the loss of such a friend, quite struck me down. Yet I was glad to think that I had brought to shore all that could be of use to me. I had now to look out for some spot where I could make my home. Halfway up the hill there was a small plain, four or five *score* feet long, and twice as broad; and as it had a full view of the sea, I thought it would be a good place for my house.

HOW I MADE MYSELF A HOME ON THE ISLAND

I first dug a trench round a space which took in twelve yards; and in this I drove two rows of stakes, till they stood firm like piles, five and a half feet from the ground. I made the stakes close and tight with bits of rope, and put small sticks on the top of them in the shape of spikes. This made so strong a fence that no man or beast could get in.

The door of my house was on top, and I had to climb up to it by steps, which I took in with me, so that no one else might come up by the same way. Close to the back of the house stood a sand rock, in which I made a cave, and laid all the earth that I had dug out of it round my house, to the height of a foot and a half. I had to go out once a day in search of food. The first time, I saw some goats, but they were too shy to let me get near them.

At first I thought that, for the lack of pen and ink, I should lose all note of time; so I made a large post, in the shape of a cross, on which I cut these words: "I came on shore here on the 30th of September, 1659." On the side of this post I made a notch each day, and this I kept up till the last.

I have not yet said a word of my four pets, which were two cats, a dog, and a parrot. You may guess how fond I was of them, for they were all the friends left to me. I brought the dog and two cats from the ship. The dog would fetch things for me at all times, and by his bark, his whine, his growl, and his tricks, he would all but talk to me; yet he could not give me thought for thought.

If I could have had some one near me to find fault with, or to find fault with me, what a treat it would have been!

I was a long way out of the course of ships; and oh! how dull it was to be cast on this lone spot with no one to love, no one to make me laugh, no one to make me weep, no one to make me think. It was dull to roam, day by day, from the wood to the shore, and from the shore back to the wood, and feed on my own thoughts all the while.

So much for the sad view of my case; but like most things, it had a bright side as well as a dark one. For here I was safe on land, while all the rest of the ship's crew were lost. True, I am cast on a rough and rude part of the globe, but there are no beasts of prey on it to kill or hurt me. God has sent the ship so near to me that I have got from it all things to meet my wants for the rest of my days. Let life be what it may, there is sure to be much to thank God for. And I soon gave up all dull thoughts, and did not so much as look out for a sail.

My goods from the wreck had been in the cave for more than ten months; and it was time now to put them right, as they took up all the space, and left me no room to turn in: so I made my small cave a large one, and dug it out a long way back in the sand rock.

Then I brought the mouth of the cave up to my fence, and so made a back way to my house. This done I put shelves on each side, to hold my goods, which made the cave look like a shop full of stores. To make these shelves was a very difficult task and took a long time; for to make a board, I was forced to cut down a whole tree, and chop away with my ax until one side was flat, and then cut at the other side till the board was thin enough, when I smoothed it with my adze. But in this way, out of each tree I would only get one plank. I made for myself also a table and a chair, and finally got my castle, as I called it, in very good order.

I usually rose early and set to work till noon, then I ate my meal, then I went out with my gun, and to work once more till the sun had set; and then to bed. It took me more than a week to change the shape and size of my cave. Unfortunately I made it far too large, for later on the earth fell in from the roof; and had I been in it when this took place, I should have lost my life. I had now to set up posts in my cave, with planks on the top of them, so as to make a roof of wood.

HOW I SUPPLIED MY NEEDS

I had to go to bed at dusk, till I made a lamp of goat's fat, which I put in a clay dish; and this, with a piece of hemp for a wick, made a good light. As I had found a use for the bag which had held the fowl's food on board ship, I shook out from it the husks of corn. This was just at the time when the great rains fell, and in the course of a month, blades of rice, and corn, and rye sprang up. As time went by, and the grain was ripe, I kept it, and took care to sow it each year; but I could not boast of a crop of wheat for three years.

I knew that tools would be my first want, and that I should have to grind mine on the stone, as they were blunt and worn with use. But as it took both hands to hold the tool, I could not turn the stone; so I made a wheel by which I could move it with my foot. This was no small task, but I took great pains with it, and at length it was done.

I had now been in the isle twelve months, and I thought it was time to go all round it in search of its woods, springs, and creeks. So I set off and brought back with me limes and grapes in their prime, large and ripe. I had hung the grapes in the sun to dry, and in a few days' time went to fetch them, that I might lay up a store. The *vale*, on the banks of which they grew, was fresh and green, and a clear bright stream ran through it, which gave so great a charm to the spot as to make me wish to live there.

But there was no view of the sea from the vale, while from my house no ships could come on my side of the isle and not be seen by me; yet the cool, soft banks were so sweet and new to me that much of my time was spent there.

In the first of the three years in which I had grown corn, I had sown it too late; in the next it was spoilt by the *drought;* but the third year's crop had sprung up well.

Few of us think of the cost at which a loaf of bread is made. Of course, there was no plow here to turn up the earth, and no spade to dig it with, so I made one with wood; but this was soon worn out, and for want of a rake, I made use of the bough of a tree. When I had got the corn home, I had to *thresh* it, part the grain from the *chaff,* and store it up. Then came the want of *sieves* to clean it, of a mill to grind it, and of yeast to make bread of it.

If I could have found a large stone, slightly hollow on top, I might, by pounding the grain on it with another round stone, have made a very good meal. But all the stones I could find were too soft, and in the end I had to make a sort of mill of hard wood, in which I burned a hollow place, and on that pounded the grain into meal with a heavy stick.

Baking I did by building a big fire, then raking away the ashes, and putting the dough on the hot place, covered with a kind of basin made of clay, over which I had heaped the red ashes.

Thus my bread was made, though I had no tools; and no one could say that I did not earn it by the sweat of my brow. When the rain kept me indoors, it was good fun to teach my pet bird Poll to talk; but so mute were all things round me that the sound of my own voice made me start.

My chief wants now were jars, pots, cups, and plates, but I knew not how I could make them. At last I went in search of clay, and found a bank of it a mile from my house; but it was quite a joke to see the queer shapes and forms that I made out of it. For some of my pots and jars were too weak to bear their own weight; and they would fall out here, and in there, in all sorts of ways; while some, when they were put in the sun to bake, would crack with the heat of its rays. You may guess what my joy was when at last a pot was made which would stand the fire so that I could boil the meat for *broth.*

The next thing to turn my thoughts to was the ship's boat, which lay on the high ridge of sand, where it had been thrust by the storm which had cast me on these shores. But it lay with the keel to the sky, so I had to dig the sand from it, and turn it up with the help of a pole. When I had done this, I found it was all in vain, for I had not the strength to launch it. So all I could do now was to make a boat of less size out of a tree; and I found one that was just fit for it, which grew not far from the shore, but I could no more stir this than I could the ship's boat.

"Well," thought I, "I must give up the boat, and with it all my hopes to leave the isle. But I have this to think of: I am lord of the whole isle; in fact, a king. I have wood with which I might build a fleet, and grapes, if not corn, to freight it with, though all my wealth is but a few gold coins." For these I had no sort of use, and could have found it in my heart to give them all for a peck of peas and some ink, which last I stood much in need of. But it was best to dwell more on what I had than on what I had not.

I now must needs try once more to build a boat, but this time it was to have a mast for which the ship's sails would be of great use. I made a deck at each end to keep out the spray of the sea, a bin for my food, and a rest for my gun, with a flap to screen it from the wet. More than all, the

boat was one of such a size that I could launch it.

My first cruise was up and down the creek, but soon I got bold, and made the whole round of my isle. I took with me bread, cakes, a pot full of rice, and half a goat, and two great coats, one of which was to lie on, and one to put on at night. I set sail in the sixth year of my reign. On the east side of the isle there was a large ridge of rocks which lay two miles from the shore, and shoal of sand lay for a half a mile from the rocks to the beach. To round to this point I had to sail a great way out to sea; and here I all but lost my life.

But I got back to my home at last. On my way there, quite worn out with the toils of the boat, I lay down in the shade to rest my limbs, and slept. But judge, if you can, what a start I gave when a voice woke me out of my sleep, and spoke my name three times! A voice in this wild place! To call me by name, too! Then the voice said "Robin! Robin Crusoe! Where are you? Where have you been? How came you here?" But now I saw it all; for at the top of the hedge sat Poll, who did but say the words she had been taught by me.

I now went in search of some goats, and laid snares for them with rice for a bait. I had set the traps in the night, and found they had all stood, though the bait was all gone. So I thought of a new way to take them, which was to make a pit and lay sticks and grass on it, so as to hide it; and in this way I caught an old goat and some kids. But the old goat was much too *fierce* for me, so I let him go.

I brought all the young ones home, and let them fast a long time, till at last they fed from my hand and were quite tame. I kept them in a kind of park, in which there were trees to screen them from the sun. At first my park was half a mile round; but it struck me that, in so great a space, the kids would soon get as wild as if they had the range of the whole vale, and that it would be as well to give them less room; so I had to make a hedge, which took me three months to plant. My park held a flock of twelve goats, and in two years more there were more than two score.

My dog sat at meals with me, and one cat on each side of me on stools, and we had Poll to talk to us. Now for a word or two as to the dress in which I made a tour round the isle. I could but think how droll it would look in the streets of the town in which I was born.

I usually wore a high cap of goat's skin, with a long flap that hung down, to keep the sun and rain from my neck, a coat made from the skin of a goat too, the skirts of which came down to my hips, and the same on my legs, with no shoes, but flaps of the fur round my shins. I had a broad belt of the same round my waist, which drew on with two thongs; and from it, on my right side, hung a saw and an ax; and on my left side a pouch for the shot. My beard had not been cut since I came here. But no more need be said of my looks, for there were few to see me.

HOW I DISCOVERED A FOOTPRINT AND SAVED FRIDAY

A strange sight was now in store for me, which was to change the whole course of my life in the isle.

One day at noon, while on a stroll down to a part of the shore that was new to me, what should I see on the sand but the print of a man's foot! I felt as if I was bound by a spell, and could not stir from the spot.

By-and-by, I stole a look around me, but no one was in sight. What could this mean? I went three or four times to look at it. There it was--the print of a man's foot; toes, heel, and all the parts of a foot. How could it have come there?

My head swam with fear; and as I left the spot, I made two or three steps, and then took a look around me; then two steps more, and did the same thing. I took fright at the stump of an old tree, and ran to my house, as if for my life. How could aught in the shape of a man come to that shore, and I not know it? Where was the ship that brought him? Then a vague dread took hold of my mind, that some man, or set of men, had found me out; and it might be that they meant to kill me, or rob me of all I had.

Fear kept me indoors for three days, till the want of food drove me out. At last I was so bold as to go down to the coast to look once more at the print of the foot, to see if it was the same shape as my own. I found it was not so large by a great deal; so it was clear that it was not one of my own footprints and that there were men in the isle.

One day as I went from the hill to the coast, a scene lay in front of me which made me sick at heart. The spot was spread with the bones of men. There was a round place dug in the earth, where a fire had been made, and here some men had come to feast. Now that I had seen this sight, I knew not how to act; I kept close to my home, and would scarce stir from it save to milk my flock of goats.

A few days later I was struck by the sight of some smoke, which came from a

fire no more than two miles off. From this time I lost all my peace of mind. Day and night a dread would haunt me that the men who had made this fire would find me out. I went home and drew up my steps, but first I made all things round me look wild and rude. To load my gun was the next thing to do, and I thought it would be best to stay at home and hide.

But this was not to be borne long. I had no spy to send out, and all I could do was to get to the top of the hill and keep a good look-out. At last, through my glass, I could see a group of wild men join in a dance round their fire. As soon as they had

glass that there were a score and a half at least on the east side of the isle. They had meat on the fire round which I could see them dance. They then took a man from one of the boats, who was bound hand and foot; but when they loosed his bonds, he set off as fast as his feet would take him, and in a straight line to my house.

To tell the truth, when I saw all the rest of the men run to catch him my hair stood on end with fright. In the creek he swam like a fish, and the plunge which he took brought him through it in a few strokes. All the men now gave up the chase but two, and they swam through the creek, but by no means so fast as the slave had done.

Now, I thought, was the time for me to help the poor man, and my heart told me it would be right to do so. I ran down my steps with my two guns, and went with all speed up the hill, and then down by a short cut to meet them.

I gave a sign to the poor slave to come to me, and at the same time went up to meet the two men who were in chase of him. I made a rush at the first of these, to knock him down with the stock of my gun, and he fell. I saw the one who was left aim at me with his bow, so, to save my life, I aimed carefully and shot him dead.

The smoke and noise from my gun gave the poor slave who had been bound such a shock that he stood still on the spot, as if he had been in a trance. I gave a loud shout for him to come to me. At length he came, knelt down to kiss the ground, and then took hold of my foot and set it on his head. All this meant that he was my slave; and I bade him rise and made much of him.

I did not like to take my slave to my house, nor to my cave; so I threw down some straw from the rice plant for him to sleep on, and gave him some bread and a bunch of dry grapes to eat. He was a fine man, with straight, strong limbs, tall and young. His hair was thick, like wool, and black. His head was large and high, and he had bright black eyes. He was of a dark brown hue; his face was round and his nose small, but not flat; he had a good mouth with thin lips, with which he could give a soft smile; and his teeth were as white as

left I took two guns, and slung a sword on my side; then with all speed I set off to the top of the hill, once more to have a good view.

This time I made up my mind to go up to the men, but not with a view to kill them, for I felt that it would be wrong to do so. With a heavy load of arms it took me two hours to reach the spot where the fire was; and by the time I got there the men had all gone; but I saw them in four boats out at sea.

Down on the shore, there was proof of what the work of these men had been. The signs of their feast made me sick at heart, and I shut my eyes. I durst not fire my gun when I went out for food on that side the isle, lest there should be some of the men left, who might hear it, and so find me out.

From this time all went well with me for two years; but it was not to last. One day, as I stood on the hill, I saw six boats on the shore. What could this mean? And what had they come for? I saw through my snow.

Toward evening I had been out to milk my goats, and when he saw me he ran to me and lay down on the ground to show his thanks. He then put his head on the ground and set my foot on his head, as he had done at first. He took all the means he could think of to let me know that he would serve me all his life; and I gave a sign to make him understand that I thought well of him.

The next thing was to think of some name to call him by. I chose that of the sixth day of the week, Friday, as he came to me on that day. I took care not to lose sight of him all that night. When the sun rose we went up to the top of the hill to look out for the men, but as we could not see them or their boats, it was clear that they had left the isle.

I now set to work to make my man a cap of hare's skin, and gave him a goat's skin to wear round his waist. It was a great source of pride to him to find that his clothes were as good as my own.

At night, I kept my guns, swords, and bow close to my side; but there was no need for this, as my slave was, in sooth, most true to me. He did all that he was set to do, with all his whole heart in the work; and I knew that he would lay down his life to save mine. What could a man do more than that? And oh, the joy to have him here to cheer me in this lone isle!

HOW FRIDAY LEARNED MY WAYS

I did my best to teach him, so like a child as he was, to do and feel all that was right. I found him *apt,* and full of fun; and he took great pains to understand and learn all that I could tell him.

One day I sent him to beat out and sift some corn. I let him see me make the bread, and he soon did all the work. I felt quite a love for his true, warm heart, and he soon learned to talk to me. One day I said, "Do the men of your tribe win in fight?" He told me, with a smile, that they did. "Well, then," said I, "how came they to let their foes take you?"

"They run one, two, three, and make go in the boat that time."

"Well, and what do the men do with those they take?"

"Eat them all up."

This was not good news for me, but I went on, and said, "Where do they take them?"

"Go the next place where they think."

"Do they come here?"

"Yes, yes, they come here, come else place too."

"Have you been here with them twice?"

"Yes, come there."

He meant the northwest side of the isle, so to this spot I took him the next day. He knew the place, and told me he was there once, and with him twelve men. To let me know this, he placed twelve stones all in a row, and made me count them.

"Are not the boats lost on your shore now and then?" He said that there was no fear, and that no boats were lost. He told me that up a great way by the moon--that is, where the moon then came up–there dwelt a tribe of white men like me, with beards. I felt sure that they must have come from Spain, to work the gold mines. I put this to him: "Could I go from this isle and join those men?"

"Yes, yes, you may go in two boats."

It was hard to see how one man could go in two boats, but what he meant was, a boat twice as large as my own.

To please my poor slave, I gave him a sketch of my whole life; I told him where I was born, and where I spent my days when a child. He was glad to hear tales of the land of my birth, and of the trade which we kept up, in ships, with all parts of the known world. I gave him a knife and a belt, which made him dance with joy.

One day as we stood on the top of the hill at the east side of the isle, I saw him fix his eyes on the main land, and stand for a long time to gaze at it; then jump and sing, and call out to me.

"What do you see?" said I.

"O joy!" said he, with a fierce glee in his eyes, "O glad! There see my land!"

Why did he strain his eyes to stare at this land as if he had a wish to be there? It put fears in my mind which made me feel far less at my ease with him. Thought I, if he should go back to his home, he will think no more of what I have taught him and done for him. He will be sure to tell the rest of his tribe all my ways, and come back with, it may be scores of them, and kill me, and then dance around me, as they did round the men the last time they came on my isle.

But these were all false fears, though they found a place in my mind a long while; and I was not so kind to him now as I had been. From this time I made it a rule, day by day, to find out if there were grounds for my fears or not. I said, "Do you wish to be once more in your own land?"

"Yes! I be much O glad to be at my own land."

"What would you do there? Would you turn wild, and be as you were?"

"No, no, I would tell them to be good, tell them eat bread, corn, milk, no eat man more!"

"Why, they would kill you!"

"No, no, they no kill; they love learn."

He then told me that some white men who had come on their shores in a boat had taught them a great deal.

"Then will you go back to your land with me?"

He said he could not swim so far, so I told him he should help me to build a boat to go in. Then he said, "If you go, I go."

"I go? why, they would eat me!"

"No, me make them much love you."

Then he told me as well as he could, how kind they had been to some white men. I brought out the large boat to hear, what he thought of it, but he said it was too small. We then went to look at the old ship's boat, which, as it had been in the sun for years, was not at all in a sound state. The poor man made sure that it would do. But how were we to know this? I told him we should build a boat as large as that, and that he should go home in it. He spoke not a word, but was grave and sad.

"What ails you?" said I.

"Why you grieve mad with your man?"

"What do you mean? I am not cross with you."

"No cross? no cross with me? Why send your man home to his own land, then?"

"Did you not tell me you would like to go back?"

"Yes, yes, we both there; no wish self there, if you not there!"

"And what should I do there?"

"You do great deal much good! You teach wild men be good men."

We soon set to work to make a boat that would take us both. The first thing was to look out for some large trees that grew near the shore, so that we could launch our boat when it was made. My slave's plan was to burn the wood to make it the right shape; but as mine was to hew it, I set him to work with my tools, and in two months time, we had made a good strong boat; but it took a long while to get her down to the shore and float her.

Friday had the whole charge of her; and, large as she was, he made her move with ease, and said,"he thought she go there well, though great blow wind!" He did not know that I meant to make a mast and sail. I cut down a young fir tree for the mast, and then I set to work at the sail. It made me laugh to see my man stand and stare, when he came to watch me sail the boat. But he soon gave a jump, a laugh, and a clap of the hands when for the first time he saw the sail jib and fall, now on this side, now on that.

The next thing to do was to stow our boat up in the creek, where we dug a small dock; and when the tide was low, we made a dam, to keep out the sea. The time of year had now come for us to set sail, so we got out all our stores, to put them in the boat.

THE ARRIVAL OF THE ENGLISH SHIP AND HOW I SAILED FOR HOME

I was fast asleep in my hutch one morning, when my man Friday came running in to me, and called aloud, "Master, master, they are come, they are come! I jumped up, and went out as soon as I could get my clothes on, through my little grove, which by the way, was by this time grown to be a very thick wood. I went without my arms, which was not my custom to do: but I was surprised when, turning my eyes to the sea, I saw a boat at about a league and a half distance, standing in for the shore, with a shoulder-of-mutton sail, as they call it, and the wind blowing pretty fair to bring them in: also I saw that they did not come from that side which the shore lay on, but from the south end of the island.

Upon this I hastily called Friday in, and bade him lie close, for we did not know yet whether they were friends or enemies. In the next place, I went in to fetch my glass, to see what I could make of them; and, having climbed up to the top of the hill, I saw a ship lying at anchor, at about two leagues from me,but not above a league and

a half from the shore. It seemed to be an English ship, and the boat looked like an English long-boat.

They ran their boat on shore upon the beach, at about half a mile from me; which was very happy for me, else they would have landed just at my door, as I may say, and would soon have beaten me out of my castle, and perhaps have *plundered* me of all I had. When they were on shore, I saw they were Englishmen; there were in all eleven men, whereof three of them I found were unarmed, and, as I thought, bound; and when the first four or five of them had jumped on shore, they took those three out of the boat as prisoners: one of the three I could see using the *gestures* of *entreaty* and *despair:* the other two, I could see, lifted up their bands and appeared concerned but not to such a degree as the first.

I was shocked and terrified at the sight of all this and knew not what the meaning of it could be. Friday called out to me in English, as well as he could, "O master! you see English mans eat prisoner as well as savage mans." "Why, Friday," said I, "do you think they are going to eat them, then?" --"yes," said Friday, "they will eat them."--"No, no," said I, "Friday; I am afraid they will murder them indeed; but you may be sure they will not eat them."

I expected to see the three prisoners killed every minute, so I fitted myself up for a battle, though with much caution, knowing that I had to do with another kind of enemy than if I were fighting savages. I ordered Friday also to load himself with arms. I took myself two fowling-pieces, and I gave him two muskets. My figure was very fierce; I had my goat-skin coat on, with the great cap, a naked sword, two pistols in my belt, and a gun upon each shoulder.

It was my design not to have made any attempt till it was dark; but about two o'clock, being the heat of the day, I found, in short, they had all gone straggling into the woods, and, as I thought, had all laid down to sleep. The three poor distressed men, too anxious for their condition to get any sleep, had, however, sat down under the shelter of a great tree.

I resolved to discover myself to them, and learn something of their condition; immediately I march toward them, my man Friday at a good distance behind me, as formidable for his arms as I, but not making quite so staring a spectre-like figure as I did. I came as near them undiscovered as I could, and then, before any of them saw me, I called aloud to them in Spanish, "Who are ye, sirs?"

They gave a start at my voice and at my strange dress, and made a move as if they would fly from me. I said, "Do not fear me, for it may be that you have a friend at hand, though you do not think it." "He must be sent from the sky then," said one of them with a grave look; and he took off his hat to me at the same time. "All help is from thence, sir," I said. "But what can I do to aid you? You look as if you had some load of grief on your breast. A moment ago I saw one of the men lift his sword as if to kill you."

The tears ran down the poor man's face, as he said, "Is this a god, or is it but a man?" Have no doubt on that score, sir," said I, "for a god would not have come with a dress like this. No, do not fear--nor raise your hopes too high; for you see but a man, yet one who will do all he can to help you. Your speech shows me that you come from the same land as I do. I will do all I can to serve you. Tell me your case."

"Our case, sir, is too long to tell you while they who would kill us are so near. My name is Paul. To be short, sir, my crew have thrust me out of my ship, which you see out there, and have left me here to die. It was as much as I could do to make them sheathe their swords, which you saw were drawn to slay me. They have set me down in this isle with these two men, my friend here, and the ship's mate."

"Where have they gone?" said I.

"There, in the wood close by. I fear they may have seen and heard us. If they have, they will be sure to kill us all."

"Have they fire-arms?"

"They have four guns, one of which is in the boat."

"Well, then leave all to me!"

"There are two of the men," said he, "who are worse than the rest. All but these I feel sure would go back to work the ship."

I thought it was best to speak out to Paul at once, and I said, "Now if I save your life, there are two things which you must do."

But he read my thoughts, and said, "If you save my life, you shall do as you like with me and my ship, and take her where you please."

I saw that the two men, in whose charge the boat had been left, had come on shore; so the first thing I did was to send Friday to fetch from it the oars, the sail, and the gun. And now the ship might be said to be in our hands. When the time came for the men to go back to the ship, they were in a great rage; for, as the boat had now no sail nor oars, they know not how to get out to the ship.

We heard them say that it was a strange sort of isle, for that sprites had come to the boat, to take off the sails and oars. We could see them run to and fro, with great rage; then go and sit in the boat to rest, and then come on shore once more. When they drew near to us, Paul and Friday would fain have had me fall on them at once. But my wish was to spare them, and kill as few as possible. I told two of my men to creep on their hands and knees close to the ground, so that they might not be seen, and when they got up to the men, not to fire till I gave the word.

They had not stood thus long when three of the crew came up to us. Till now we had but heard their voices, but when they came so near as to be seen, Paul and Friday stood up and shot at them. Two of the men fell dead, and they were the worst of the crew, and the third ran off. At the sound of the guns I came up, but it was so dark that the men could not tell if there were three of us or three score.

It fell out just as I wished, for I heard the men ask: "To whom must we yield, and where are they?" Friday told them that Paul was there with the king of the isle, who had brought with him a crowd of men! At this one of the crew said: "If Paul will spare our lives we will yield." "Then," said Friday, "you shall know the king's will." Then Paul said to them: "You know my voice; if you lay down your arms the king will spare your lives."

They fell on their knees to beg the same of me. I took good care that they did not see me, but I gave them my word that they should all live, that I should take four of them to work the ship, and that the rest would be bound hand and foot for the good faith of the four. This was to show them what a stern king I was.

Of course I soon set them free, and I put them in a way to take my place on the isle. I told them of all my ways, taught them how to mind the goats, how to work the farm and make the bread. I gave them a house to live in, firearms, tools, and my two tame cats; in fact, all that I owned but Poll and my gold.

As I sat on the top of the hill, Paul came up to me. He held out his hand to point to the ship, and with much warmth took me to his arms and said: "My dear friend, there is your ship! for this vessel is all yours, and all that is in her, and so are all of us."

I made ready to go on board the ship, but told the captain I would stay that night to get my things in shape, and asked him to go on board in the meantime and keep things right on the ship.

I cast my eyes to the ship, which rode half a mile off the shore, at the mouth of the creek, and near the place where I had brought my raft to land. Yes, there she stood, the ship that was to set me free and to take me where I might choose to go. She set her sails to the wind and her flags threw out their gay stripes in the breeze. Such a sight was too much for me, and I fell down faint with joy.

Friday and Paul then went on board the ship, and Paul took charge of her once more. We did not start that night, but at noon the next day I left the isle--that lone isle, where I had spent so great a part of my life.

When I took leave of this island, I carried on board a great goat-skin cap I had made, and my parrot; also the money which had lain by me so long useless that it was grown rusty or tarnished, and could hardly pass for gold till it had been a little rubbed and handled. And thus I left the island, the 19th of December, as I found by the ship's account, in the year 1686, after I had been upon it seven-and-twenty-years, one month, and nineteen days; being delivered from this second captivity the same day of the month that I first made my escape from among the Moors. In this vessel, after a long voyage. I arrived in England the 11th of June, in the year 1687, having been more than thirty-five years absent.

THINKING IT THROUGH

1. What is initiative?
2. Did Robinson Crusoe need this important characteristic for survival? Why?
3. How can you show initiative in school? at home? in your neighborhood? among your friends? for your country?

ABOUT THE AUTHOR

Daniel Defoe (1659-1731), a noted English journalist and author, was born in St. Giles parish, Cripplegate, London. Although he wrote almost incessantly throughout his varied and eventful life, his most famous work is the immortal classic, *Robinson Crusoe*.

THE NOBLEST MEN

— Author Unknown

The noblest men that live on earth,
   Are men whose hands are brown with toil;
Who, backed by no ancestral graves,
   Hew down the woods, and till the soil;
And win thereby a prouder name
Than follows king's or warrior's fame.

The working men, whate'er their task,
   Who carve the stone or bear the hod,
They wear upon their honest brows
   The royal stamp and seal of God;
And worthier are their drops of sweat
Than diamonds in a *coronet*.

God bless the noble working men,
   Who rear the cities of the plain;
Who dig the mines, who build the ships,
   And drive the *commerce* of the main!
God bless them! for their toiling hands
Have wrought the glory of all lands.

coronet — crown
commerce — business

> If people speak ill of you, live so that no one will believe them.
> —Plato

Respect is an attribute which every person desires others to render to him.
Read carefully and thoughtfully to discover the true meaning of respect.

RESPECT

— Author Unknown

You must first learn to respect yourself. When you feel respect for your real self, you are unwilling to do a mean thing. You wish your parents, your teachers, and your friends to think highly of you; and you understand that they cannot think highly of you unless your every act is honorable. Moreover, if you wish your friends to feel respect for you, you must show courteous *consideration* and *respect* for them, and for their rights.

Especially should young people *reverence* old age without regard to station, dress, or sex. They should do this for their own sakes as well as for the sake of those who begin to feel that they are in the way in the world.

You will probably be old some day; and, naturally, you will wish to be respected. Consider, then, the feelings of the old while you are young. Be kind. Lend a helping hand to the old and feeble. Listen respectfully when they speak, and be thoughtful of them always. No really great man ever fails to show this consideration.

The following incident is told of President Cleveland:

In 1896, on the one hundred fiftieth anniversary of the founding of Princeton University, the graduates of former years came from far and near for a reunion. President Cleveland reviewed the long line of alumni as they marched by: the class of '96 with its hundreds of shouting young fellows, the class of '95, the other classes in order down through the 90's, the 80's, the 70's, and the 60's, etc., the ranks growing thinner according to the age of the class. As the gray-haired veteran representatives of the noble old college passed the reviewing stand, President Cleveland uncovered his head as a token of respect for old age, and remained uncovered in the chilly night air until the last man had slowly filed by. This was a beautiful tribute of respect, and it was a lesson in politeness that all young people might well learn.

All oriental peoples, particularly the Japanese and the Chinese, have from *remote* ages felt and shown great respect for old people; and the world to-day points to China and Japan as models of behavior in this regard. Young Americans must take care not to be outdone by the Chinese and Japanese in showing consideration for the aged.

Here follows a pleasing incident which shows what a self-respecting young Filipino is capable of:

It was May in Manila, toward the end of a hot day. The Bagumbayan drive was thronged with all sorts of vehicles from caretelas and rumbling trucks to *victorias*, screeching automobiles, and clanging electric cars. On the west side of the drive stood a *timid* old woman in wild confusion, wishing to cross to the other side but fearing to *venture*, and protesting excitedly by voice and *gesture* against all the assurances of her younger companion.

Just then there came along a young man in a spotless white suit—apparently a student from either the Normal or the High School. He saw the old woman's plight—a woman as old as his own grandmother. Without a moment's hesitation that fine upstanding student put one strong, young arm about that poorly clad, feeble old figure and took her hands in his as if to give her confidence. Then carefully, patiently, looking first to the right and then to the left, he threaded his way in and out among the vehicles to the opposite side of the drive with his charge. There he landed her safely.

I watched him as he raised his hat to her with the same respect that he would show to the finest lady in the land, and turned and went modestly about his business as if nothing unusual had happened.

That young man would be worth knowing. I should like to have him for a friend. He would make a good friend and a kind neighbor. He thinks right. He feels right. He acts right. He put himself in that old woman's place, and knew how she felt; and he knew how he would wish to see his own mother or grandmother treated if she were in the same situation.

remote — distant
victorias — low, four-wheeled carriages
timid — shy
venture — undertake the risk
gesture — motion

THINKING IT THROUGH

1. What can you do for your parents and grandparents to show your respect for them?
2. Can you think of ways you can show respect to people you do not know personally?
3. This Filipino lad proved himself worth knowing by this one thoughtful act. What will people think of you by observing your actions?
4. How can you help other young Americans have respect for themselves? for others?

Theodore Roosevelt once said, "Of course, what we have a right to expect of an American boy is that he shall turn out to be a good American man. Now, the chances are great that he won't be much of a man unless he is a good deal of a boy. He must not be a coward or a weakling, a bully, a shirk or a prig. He must work hard and play hard. He must be clean-minded and clean-lived, and able to hold his own under all circumstances and against all comers. In life as in a football game the principle to follow is: Hit the line hard. Don't foul, and don't shirk — but hit the line hard!"

A former scout leader writes to his scout troop back home about the importance of discipline in life. Notice his optimistic attitude toward correction. As you read the letter, look for ways in which the Cave Scout shows a good attitude.

THE CAVE SCOUT

Dear Gang:

Surprised, were you, when you pushed back the old bear-skin curtain and crawled in, expecting to see the old Cave Scout poking up the fire? I'm sorry to miss you, fellows, but you see I've changed my address. I just couldn't be there to join in our usual confab, so I've sent this letter as the next best thing, and had it posted where you will all be sure to see it. Just stick around and make yourselves at home.

If you fellows could be any place you wanted to be today, what place would you choose? Oh, I know your answer just as well as though I were there to hear it. IN THE ARMY! Well, that's just the way I felt about it, too, so I joined the army. I'm at an officers' training camp, working harder than I ever worked before, lining up for "chow" three times a day, and having just the bulliest kind of a time. Tell you what, fellows, it's great to feel sure that you're

doing everything you can to help win this war. No soldiers ever fought in a better cause—and if I'm any judge of men, no better soldiers ever fought in any cause. Since coming here and seeing a sample of Uncle Sam's army, I think I know why the boys who are lucky enough to be in France are fighting like wildcats.

I wish I had some of you fellows with me! The ones I have in mind are those who have written to me complaining about the discipline in their troops. A fellow can learn more about discipline in one week in the army than he can in ten years outside of it. We had inspection this morning, and the Cave Scout got "skinned." What is it like to be "skinned"? Well, while the other fellows are taking an afternoon off and going to the movies, a student who has been "skinned" is walking back and forth on a *monotonous* post with a rifle rubbing

monotonous — unvarying

— 61 —

holes in his shoulder. That's where the Cave Scout will be next Saturday because he had a dirty rifle. I polished that rifle until it looked to me as bright as the morning sun. I felt as proud of it as a hen with a litter of chicks, and when I heard the rifle bolts clicking along the line as the inspecting officer advanced, I could hardly wait for him to get to me. As he came abreast of me I threw the rifle into position and jerked open the bolt. The officer grabbed it, took one quick glance, and began to talk. "Dirty chamber, dirt in the stocking swivel, dust on the sights. Put this man's name down." It was the biggest surprise of my life. But I have learned now that a rifle should be cleaned in sunlight and not in the bunk room. I looked at my piece after we were dismissed and saw that the officer was right. Well, I won't mind walking the post; that's according to the rules of the game — but you can bet I won't get caught again!

DISCIPLINE! When you have spoken that one word you have described nine-tenths of military training. Maybe I can give you some idea of how *rigid* the rules are. A fellow can get "skinned" for brushing a fly off his nose while standing at attention, for having a tent peg out of line at inspection, for stopping to get a drink before reporting for duty after receiving an order, for failing to correct a man when he sees him doing wrong, for forgetting some little thing like snapping a flap on a canteen.

Do you think that seems a little unfair? Do you think the officers ought to make allowance for a little slip once in a while? Well, it does seem hard at times, and I have no doubt the officers feel that way about it themselves, but they also know that it is their duty to enforce discipline to the letter. Why? Here's the answer. Suppose an officer in the *trenches* in France should receive an order to lead his men over the top in a charge at three minutes after seven. Then suppose that instead of leaving his trenches at exactly the time set he should go out thirty seconds late. In all probability that officer and his entire command would be killed. The same thing would happen if he were careless in setting his watch and led his men out too soon.

Do you see, fellows, that no army can be an efficient army unless every soldier obeys every order immediately and carries out his instructions to the letter? It's just a matter of----

Pardon the interruption, fellows. The whistle blew, and I had to jump into my place in line in front of the barracks. We were called out for police duty. That doesn't mean going out and putting somebody under arrest. In this case it means picking up every scrap of rubbish on our company street—cigarette butts (I hate those cigarettes more than ever now), matches, scraps of paper and bits of straw. You fellows who have been in scout camps know what that means. I know, too, that you have often thought, "Aw, shucks, what's the use of being so blame particular!" Well, I don't suppose one piece of straw on a company street in Arkansas would lose the war, but leaving even one straw would mean a letting up in discipline and discipline is the thing we're working for. One little slip would lead to another, and that to still others; and in almost no time there wouldn't be any discipline at all.

But I'll tell you, fellows, this *unrelenting* discipline doesn't make a real soldier *sullen* or sore. He has *confidence* in his leaders and knows that there is some good reason for every order that is given. Of course, in a great many cases he can't tell what that reason is, but he takes it for granted that it's all right and pitches in for all he's worth to accomplish what he is told must be done. Take our own company, for instance. When we were called out to police duty a minute ago, the Cave Scout walked beside a man who left a million dollar business four weeks ago to do his bit for Uncle Sam. This man was picking up dirty

rigid — inflexible
trenches — ditches
unrelenting — unyielding
sullen — resentful
confidence — trust, faith

cigarette butts as though it was the greatest fun in the world. He walked along, humming, "Over There", and taking orders from a stocky little top sargeant who drove a truck before he enlisted in the army. That's the kind of men who are putting their whole hearts into this work of fitting themselves to command American soldiers. Do you have any doubt in the world that that kind of men will make good?

For my part, boys, I feel that the training in discipline we are getting is the best thing in the army. And say, if it's such a good thing for the army, wouldn't it be a good thing for the scout troops? Oh, I know you think you are getting some discipline; but from my own observation of scout troops, I know you aren't getting half as much as you need. Now discipline can be forced on you by your scout-masters, but that kind isn't worth anything as compared with the kind you force upon yourselves. Why, if every member of this good old B.S.A. would decide right now that from this time on he would obey every order of

his officers at once, in full, and gladly, you'd jump so far ahead in two weeks that you would surprise yourselves. I'd like to see that tried! Please don't think that I'm complaining about what you have done— the results obtained are something you can all feel mighty proud of. But I do know, since I have had a touch of real military training, that it is possible for you to do a great deal more.

This war probably will be over before many of you boys will have a chance to get into the army, so you will not have an opportunity to get this training in discipline as the Cave Scout is now getting. But you can start in your troops and in school. And after the war is over and the United States takes up the big job of readjusting itself to peace conditions, the need for disciplined men will be as great as it is now. Put this down as gospel truth: the fellow who doesn't know how to obey orders will never get a chance to give them, and the fellow who is not disciplined will be "out of luck," as we say in the Army.

Yours in the service of Uncle Sam,
THE CAVE SCOUT.

—From "Boys' Life," the Boy Scouts' Magazine

THINKING IT THROUGH

1. What does the author mean by saying that "the fellow who doesn't know how to obey orders will never get a chance to give them?"
2. Is discipline necessary in everyone's life? Why?
3. What does he mean by saying that "the fellow who is not disciplined will be out of luck . . . ?"
4. What is self-discipline? Explain the difference between discipline and self-discipline.
5. Do you feel that self-discipline is needed today? Why? Give an example.

THE ATHENIAN BOYS' OATH

We will never bring *disgrace* to this, our city, by any act of dishonesty or *cowardice*, nor ever desert our suffering comrades in the ranks.

We will fight for the ideals and sacred things of the city, both alone and with many.

We will revere and obey the city's laws and do our best to *incite* a like *respect* and *reverence* in those above us, who are prone to *annul* or to set them at naught.

We will strive unceasingly to quicken the public's sense of civic duty.

Thus in all these ways we will *transmit* this city not only not less, but greater, better, and more beautiful than it was transmitted to us.

annul — nullify
cowardice — lack of courage
disgrace — dishonor
incite — stir up, urge
respect — admiration, consideration
reverence — honor
transmit — pass on

THE OWL CRITIC

—James T. Fields

"Who stuffed that white owl?" No one spoke in the shop;
The barber was busy, and he couldn't stop;
The customers, waiting their turns, were all reading
The Daily, the Herald, the Post, little heeding
The young man who blurted out such a blunt question;
Not one raised his head, or even made a suggestion;
    And the barber kept on shaving.

"Don't you see, Mr. Brown,"
Cried the youth with a frown,
"How wrong the whole thing is,
"How *preposterous* each wing is,
How flattened the head is, how jammed down the neck is—
In short, the whole owl, what an ignorant wreck 'tis!
I make no apology;
I've learned owl-ecology.
I've passed days and nights in a hundred collections,
And cannot be blinded to any *deflections*
Arising from unskillful fingers that fail
To stuff a bird right, from his beak to his tail.
Mr. Brown! Mr. Brown!
Do take that bird down,
Or you'll soon be the laughing-stock all over town!"
    And the barber kept on shaving.

"I've studied owls
And other night-fowls,
And I tell you
What I know to be true;
An owl cannot roost
With his limbs so unloosed;
No owl in this world
Ever had his claws curled,
Ever had his legs slanted,
Ever had his bill canted,
Ever had his neck screwed
        Into that attitude.
        He can't do it, because
        'Tis against all bird-laws.
        Anatomy teaches,
        Ornithology preaches
        An owl has a toe
        That can't turn out so!

I've made the white owl my study for years,
And to see such a job almost moves me to tears!
Mr. Brown, I'm amazed
You should be so gone crazed
As to put up a bird
In that posture absurb!
To look at that owl really brings on a dizziness.
The man who stuffed him didn't half know his business."
    And the barber kept on shaving.

"Examine those eyes.
I'm filled with surprise
Taxidermists should pass
Off on you such poor glass;
So unnatural they seem
They'd make *Audubon* scream,
And *John Burroughs* laugh
To encounter such chaff.
Do take that bird down;
Have him stuffed again, Brown!"
    And the barber kept on shaving.

"With some sawdust and bark
I could stuff in the dark
An owl better than that.
I could make an old hat
Look more like an owl
Than that horrid fowl,
Stuck up there so stiff like a side of coarse leather;
In fact, about him there's not one natural feather."

Just then, with a wink and a sly normal lurch,
The owl, very gravely, got down from his perch,
Walked around, and regarded his fault-finding critic
(Who thought he was stuffed) with a glance *analytic*,
And then fairly hooted, as if he should say:
"Your learning's at fault this time, anyway:
Don't waste it again on a live bird, I pray.
I'm an owl; you're another. Sir Critic, good-day!"
        And the barber kept on shaving.

analytic — studied carefully
Audobon — American ornithologist
deflections — deviations
John Burroughs — American naturalist
ornithology — branch of zoology dealing with birds
preposterous — absurd
Taxidermists — persons who stuff and mount animals

THINKING IT THROUGH

1. Do you ever stop learning new things?
2. Do you think it would be wise for a young person to think he has mastered a subject and knows all there is to know about it?
3. Which should be more important in a person's life, talking or listening? Why?

ABOUT THE AUTHOR

James T. Fields, born in Portsmouth, N.H., 1816, died in Boston, 1881, was a publisher and author. He was the personal friend and adviser of Emerson, Longfellow, Whittier, Lowell, Hawthorne and Holmes, besides being himself an author of note. He was editor of the *Atlantic Monthly* from 1861 to 1871.

EACH DAY IS A NEW BEGINNING

—Susan Coolidge

Every day is a fresh beginning,
    Every morn is the world made new,
You who are weary of sorrow and sinning,
    Here is a beautiful hope for you—
    A hope for me and a hope for you.

All the past things are past and over,
    The tasks are done and the tears are shed;
Yesterday's errors let yesterday cover—
    Yesterday's wounds, which smarted and bled,
    Are healed with the healing which night has shed.

Yesterday now is a part of forever
    Bound up in a sheaf which God holds tight,
With glad days and sad days and bad days which never
    Shall visit us more with their bloom and their blight—
    Their fullness of sunshine or sorrowful night.

Let them go since we cannot re-live them,
    Cannot undo and cannot atone,
God in His mercy receive and forgive them!
    Just the new days are our own—
    Today is ours and today alone.

Every day is a fresh beginning,
    Listen, my soul, to the glad refrain,
And spite of old sorrows and older sinning,
    And puzzles forecasted and possible pain,
    Take heart with the day and begin again.

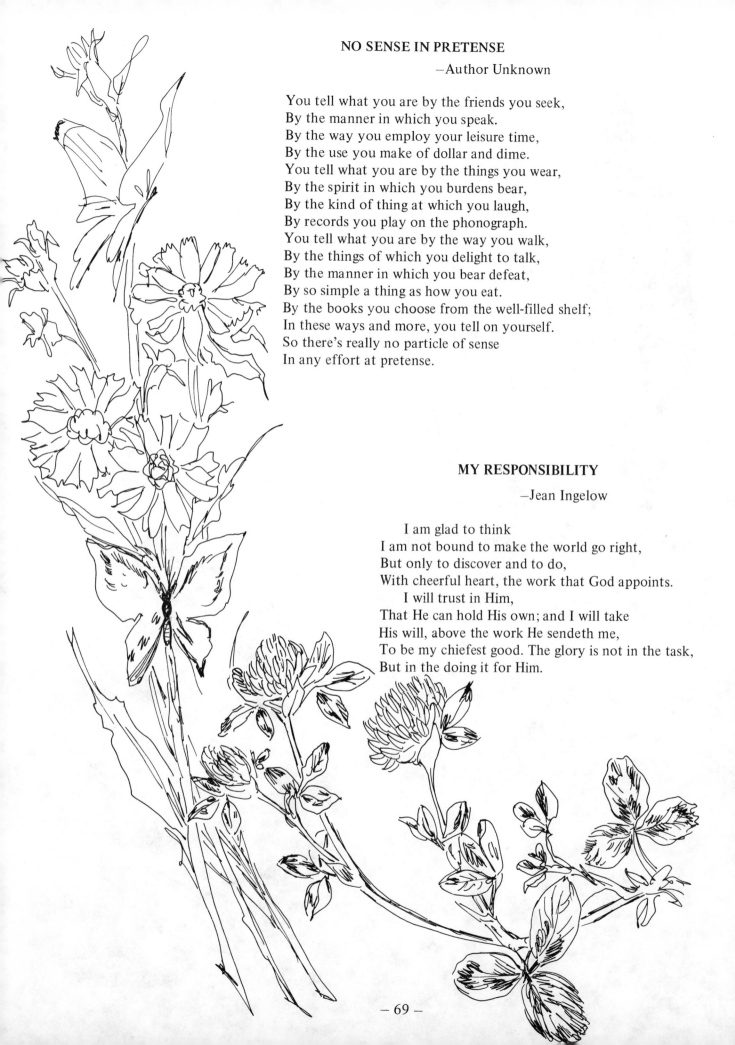

NO SENSE IN PRETENSE

—Author Unknown

You tell what you are by the friends you seek,
By the manner in which you speak.
By the way you employ your leisure time,
By the use you make of dollar and dime.
You tell what you are by the things you wear,
By the spirit in which you burdens bear,
By the kind of thing at which you laugh,
By records you play on the phonograph.
You tell what you are by the way you walk,
By the things of which you delight to talk,
By the manner in which you bear defeat,
By so simple a thing as how you eat.
By the books you choose from the well-filled shelf;
In these ways and more, you tell on yourself.
So there's really no particle of sense
In any effort at pretense.

MY RESPONSIBILITY

—Jean Ingelow

I am glad to think
I am not bound to make the world go right,
But only to discover and to do,
With cheerful heart, the work that God appoints.
I will trust in Him,
That He can hold His own; and I will take
His will, above the work He sendeth me,
To be my chiefest good. The glory is not in the task,
But in the doing it for Him.

THE FLAG GOES BY

–Henry Holcomb Bennet

Hats off!
Along the street there comes
A blare of bugles, a ruffle of drums,
A flash of color beneath the sky:
Hats off!
The flag is passing by!

Blue and *crimson* and white it shines,
Over the steel-tipped, ordered lines.
Hats off!
The colors before us fly;
But more than the flag is passing by.

Sea-fights and land-fights, *grim* and great,
Fought to make and to save the State:
Weary marches and sinking ships;
Cheers of victory on dying lips;

Days of plenty and years of peace;
March of a strong land's swift increase;
Equal justice, right and law,
Stately honor and *reverend awe;*

Sign of a nation, great and strong
Toward her people from foreign wrong:
Pride and glory and honor,—all
Live in the colors to stand or fall.

Hats off!
Along the street there comes
A blare of bugles, a ruffle of drums;
And *loyal* hearts are beating high:
Hats off!
The flag is passing by!

crimson - deep red
grim - fierce
stately honor - unapproachable purity
reverend awe - deep, reverent wonder
loyal - faithful

This is the story of a boy who came to America from Denmark.
He served his new country unselfishly in many useful ways. Years later President
Theodore Roosevelt said that he was the most useful citizen in America.
As you read his story, find the qualities that
made Jacob Riis such an outstanding American.

JACOB RIIS

—Lawrence McTurnan

Would you like to know the story of the man whom President Roosevelt once called "The most useful citizen in the world . . . ?" This is the story:

Jacob Riis was born of poor parents in the little kingdom of Denmark across the seas. His father was a carpenter who earned a scant living by his daily wage. Jacob went to school and also learned his father's trade.

He read and heard a great deal about the wonderful country of America and of the opportunities which this comparatively new country gave to young men. He talked to his parents about his desire to go to America and they finally gave their consent for him to make the venture.

Wages were not very high in Denmark and he had not earned much money. He had only enough to pay his fare on the boat to America and to buy a large navy revolver.

He had read some wild west stories of Indian fights and buffalo hunts. He thought New York was the center of these exciting scenes and that he would have to protect himself by shooting wild animals almost as soon as he arrived there. He carried the revolver in plain view, hanging out of his coat pocket. He wanted to have it where he could get it instantly when he saw either a bear, buffalo, or Indian coming at him.

When he landed from the boat and started up Broadway, a policeman stopped him and in a kindly manner told him that he had better put the revolver away as he did not need it.

"Besides," said the officer, "if you carry it out where people can see it some one may steal it."

Jacob used the revolver just once, but not for shooting, as you will learn later. In after years he saw how foolish he had acted and he laughingly said, "I was very green."

There was plenty of work to do in the new and strange country but it was hard for Jacob to get a job. His English was poor and his foreign accent was strong. He did not know the ways of Americans and he had but little success in securing work. At last he fell in with some men who were going to work in the coal mines near Pittsburgh. He went along and helped build houses for the miners.

After a few days' work as a carpenter he decided to work in the mines. The first and only day he worked in the mines he was almost killed by a cave-in and he quit the job.

At that time the Franco-Prussian War had begun and he was anxious to help France. He went to Buffalo to enlist in the French army but there he was advised to go to New York City to see French officials.

He arrived in New York with only one cent in his pocket. His efforts to get into the war met with failure and he was left without money or work. He pawned his revolver and his boots to pay for one night's lodging.

He tried to get work and did many things. He worked on a truck farm, in a brick yard and on a clay bank. He quit his work and again he tried to get into the French army but was unsuccessful.

He now had nothing but his grip sack, a linen duster and a pair of socks. He wandered about looking for work. He was hungry and looked like a tramp but he would not beg as he had only *contempt* for tramps. He believed that every man should earn his living and in all his hunger and cold and misery he held to this principle.

At last he became homesick and discouraged. He almost sank into despair and while in this condition he went out to the brink of the river and sat down, wet, cold and disheartened. While he sat there, a little stray dog came up to him, licked him in the face and lay down beside him.

contempt — disrespect

"The dog," said he years later, "was the bright spot in my life." The dog seemed to tell him that there was one who understood him and that he was not alone. He picked the dog up under his arm and left the river. A new hope came into his life.

That night at midnight he went to the police station in Mulberry Street and asked for lodging. The police officer allowed him to sleep there but the dog was not admitted. The little dog watched on the step all night for his master. Jacob slept in the basement or cellar of the police station where the toughest men went for a night's rest when they had nowhere else to go.

About two o'clock in the morning he felt something pull at his neck and upon examination he found that a thief had stolen a gold chain and a locket which his mother had given him. The next morning he complained to the officer, who in turn accused the boy of theft and ordered him out of the station. The doorkeeper put him out so roughly that the boy fought back. The little dog, who had been waiting all night for his companion in misery, saw the situation and jumped to the defense of his master. He bit the stranger's leg. The jailer grabbed the dog by the hind legs, swung him over his shoulders and beat his brains out on the stone step.

Jacob was so angry at this cruel and inhuman treatment of his little defender that he shook his fists at the man and told him he would get even with him some day. And he kept his promise.

He became a peddler and first sold tables, then books and flat-irons. One day a man offered him a place as a reporter on the Brooklyn News and in this work he found what he liked to do. He enjoyed writing the news and he believed he saw an opportunity to do a good service.

After working as a reporter for some time, he saved seventy-five dollars and made a proposition to the owner to buy the paper. At first he was laughed at, but he was serious and persistent and finally arranged to buy it by turning over what cash he had and giving his notes for the balance of the amount due.

The News was a small paper but he soon doubled the circulation by publishing the plain facts about people. He told the truth no matter whom it hurt. He was determined to help make New York a cleaner city. The names of people who would not pay their honest debts were published in his paper. He opposed those who had wicked schemes to get people's money. He went about to see how people were living in the city. He publicly condemned places of vice and crime and he put to shame the men who built tenement houses with but little provision for light or fresh air. In one place he found fifteen people living in two rooms where not more than four or five should live and among these roomers was a baby only one week old. He carried his camera with him and took pictures of these places of sin and shame which he printed in his paper.

Now came a hard test in Jacob Riis' life! The schemers and grafters did not like the frankness and fairness of this newspaper. They hoped to control the paper and have it support their crooked deals. He could have become a rich man if he had only been willing to wink at evils, but he preferred to remain poor and to serve his fellow men in an honest way. His honor was not for sale.

He helped to create *legislation* which forced the landlords to give light and air to the tenement dwellers and to establish more schools and playgrounds for the children. He made small but beautiful parks with trees and flower beds where before were dingy buildings and dark and dangerous alleys. Mulberry Bend, known as one of the worst places in the city, was, through the influence of Mr. Riis, *converted* into a park. At the cost of millions he forced the city to provide pure water free from filth and disease-breeding germs.

Fifty thousand children were out of school in this one city. These children were, for the most part, thrown into evil influences. Hundreds of them lived and played in and around saloons where men were drinking and gambling. Such children were robbed of the opportunity in life

which the founders of our country intended they should have. Riis and other good men had laws passed compelling children to attend school.

The vicious spots of former days known as "Bandit's Roost," "Hell's Kitchen," and "Bottle Alley" were demolished in his crusade and now they are things of the past because someone cared and had the courage to battle bravely against the evils that were injuring the youth of their country.

When Mr. Riis was in the midst of his crusade, Theodore Roosevelt, who was then Police Commissioner of New York City, called at his office to see him and to offer his assistance. He did not find Mr. Riis but he left his card, which said, "I have come to help." This was the beginning of a lifelong friendship and a helpful comradeship in the service of their city and their country. Mr. Riis said that no man ever helped him to clean the slums of the city as much as did Mr. Roosevelt.

One night, Mr. Riis asked Mr. Roosevelt to go with him on a tour of inspection. Among the places they visited was the police station where Jacob's little dog had been slain by the policeman many years

legislation — laws
converted — changed

before. He led Mr. Roosevelt down into the basement and showed him where he lay when his locket and chain were stolen. He pointed out to Roosevelt where the fight took place and the stone step where the dog was killed. When Roosevelt heard the story, he struck his fists together and said: "It will never happen again for I will close this foul place tomorrow." The next morning, this police station was closed, never to be opened again.

When Mr. Riis died in 1914, Roosevelt said of him: "If I were asked to name a fellow man who came nearest to being the ideal American citizen, I should name Jacob Riis."

Mankind is a debtor to this foreign-born boy who lived to serve, and America is a better and happier country because of his life.

THINKING IT THROUGH

1. What does persistence mean? How did persistence pay off in Jacob Riis' life?
2. Why did he refuse to beg when times were hard?
3. It was said that Jacob Riis could have become rich, "if he had been willing to wink at evils, but he preferred to remain poor" and be honest. What does this reveal about him?
4. The author says, "His honor was not for sale." Explain the meaning of this statement.
5. This is the story of a man "who lived to serve." Can a person really find satisfaction in life by giving?

Accomplishing things that someone said could
not be done has brought success to thousands of people.
How can you apply the challenge of this poem in your studies,
in your home, in your sports activities?

SOMEBODY SAID IT COULDN'T BE DONE
—Edgar A. Guest

Somebody said it couldn't be done,
  But he, with a chuckle, replied
That maybe it couldn't, but he would be one
  Who wouldn't say so till he'd tried.
He waded right in with a trace of a grin
  On his face—if he worried he hid it,
He started to sing as he tackled the thing
  That couldn't be done—and he did it.

Somebody said, "Oh, you'll never do that,
  At least no one ever has done it."
But he took off his coat and he took off his hat
  And the first thing we knew, he'd begun it.
With a lift of the chin and a bit of a grin
  Without any doubting or "quit it,"
He started to sing as he tackled the thing
  That couldn't be done—and he did it.

There are thousands to tell you it cannot be done,
  There are thousands to prophesy failure,
There are thousands to point out to you, one by one,
  The dangers that wait to assail you.
But just buckle in with a lift of the chin,
  Take off your coat and go to it,
Starting to sing as you tackle the thing
  That cannot be done—and you'll do it.

Louis Pasteur refused to quit until he had achieved his goal. Time after time he failed,
but he patiently tried again and again until he succeeded.
This was the secret of his success. His outstanding work in scientific research benefits
your life every day.

LOUIS PASTEUR

—Lawrence McTurnam

The soldiers of the third regiment of Napoleon's vast armies were known for their great courage and bravery. The men were called, "The Brave amongst the Braves." One of these men was named Jean Joseph Pasteur, who had fought in many a campaign under the illustrious leader.

When Napoleon was at last defeated at the Battle of Waterloo by the English General, the Duke of Wellington, Joseph Pasteur went back to his own country to be discharged from the army.

When he reached home he entered the tannery trade which his father and grandfather had followed before him. In due time he married a village maiden. This young couple moved to Dole and there was born in 1822, the little son, Louis Pasteur, who was one day to make the whole world his debtor. This son who was born of a brave father was one day to show bravery also, not upon the battle field but in the field of science.

The boy, Louis, was reared carefully in a

home of love and devotion. His parents were poor people but they felt that it was almost as necessary to educate their children as it was to feed them and it was decided early that Louis should have a thorough college training. His mind worked so carefully that he was considered slow. He never stated anything of which he was not absolutely sure.

He was a thoughtful boy and was known as a worker. When he was in college he wrote home to his sisters, "When one is accustomed to work it is impossible to do without it." At another time he wrote: "These three things, Will, Work, Success, fill human existence. Will opens the door to success, both brilliant and happy; Work passes these doors, and at the end Success comes to crown one's efforts."

Louis was a dutiful and loving son and brother. He kept in close touch with his parents and sisters as long as they lived. He wrote to them and visited them often and he shared with them in detail his interesting experiences of life. He was known as a kind hearted man with tender affections for all his friends and loved ones. In studying the life of this great man one often thinks of the poet's couplet:

> "The tenderest are the bravest
> The loving are the daring."

Chemistry received his chief attention in college as he intended to devote his life to this subject, but after he had made much advancement in it his course was turned to the study of phases of biology in which work he was to move the whole world forward.

His work in chemistry brought him into the study of fermentation. Fermentation was not then understood. When a change took place in foods or animal matter it was called spontaneous generation, which meant that life sprang out of the substance itself without life being brought to it.

Pasteur developed the theory that the air is full of germs and that when these germs come into contact with nutriment they thrive and multiply. The scientists of his time hooted at such an idea. They said if millions of germs were in the air they

would be so thick that one could not see through them.

He would not be discouraged or driven from his conviction. He boiled yeast water in glass flasks which had small mouths. When the fluid boiled he melted the mouths of the vessels and closed them so that the air could not reach the inside. He tested the effect of the air at different altitudes upon the contents of the flasks. He opened some of them in crowded places where the air was foul and he found that changes took place rapidly in the yeast water. He then climbed high into the Alps mountains and opened the flasks, exposing the contents to the mountain air. He would then seal the flasks again before going down into the valley. He discovered that the mountain air seldom changed the fluid, while in the air at low altitudes where the dust and impurities were thicker the specimens were always altered.

Pasteur met with much opposition to his theory and his proofs for there were many who still refused to believe that microbes could be floating in the air. His critics preferred to hold to the old theory of spontaneous generation, but Pasteur

kept on and on with his experiments and proofs until finally the whole world was forced to accept the facts which he so clearly and forcefully demonstrated.

In 1865, the French Government requested Pasteur to study the silkworm disease and if possible to eradicate it. The disease was ruining the great silk industry of France.

Silk was first produced in China four thousand years ago, and for hundreds of years no nation except China knew the secrets of the silk industry. Finally the industry spread to other countries and it became one of the great sources of wealth to France. Suddenly all these riches fell away. A mysterious disease was destroying the nurseries. No one knew where the disease came from or what caused it. All were in the dark.

The discovery of the cause of this disease and its remedy was the work assigned to Pasteur. He cheerfully and patriotically went at the task. He studied and worked early and late with the microscope in his laboratory for several years, when at last he announced the method of prevention. Again, he was doubted by many scientists and business men, but his

claims were established finally beyond question, the silkworms were saved, and the wheels of the great industry were again set in motion.

Pasteur was stricken with paralysis in 1868. His family and friends thought he could not get well. His whole left side was as if dead. He expressed but one regret, and this expression reminds one of the last words of Captain Nathan Hale, which were: "I regret that I have but one life to give to my country." Pasteur said: "I am sorry to die; I wanted to do much more for my country." Pasteur had his wish for his greatest achievements were still ahead of him. He regained his health and returned to his work with his usual vigor. Only a slight lameness in one leg and stiffness in one hand remained as marks of his sickness.

Between 1867 and 1870 a dreaded disease known as anthrax or splenic fever attacked the cattle, horses and sheep in Europe. In one province in Russia more than fifty thousand cattle died of this epidemic. Pasteur attacked this disease. He studied a drop of the diseased blood under the microscope. He discovered that anthrax is a germ disease. He experimented on hundreds of cattle and sheep and found that if victims of anthrax were buried in the fields the earthworms would bring the germs to the surface and the following spring after the burial, cattle or sheep grazing over these graves would be attacked by anthrax.

It is interesting to know that the same year in which Pasteur discovered the earthworms as germ carriers from the graves to the surface of the earth, Darwin, the great English scientist, pronounced the earthworm as nature's great plow.

Pasteur experimented by taking the blood of a diseased sheep and after weakening it, injected a small amount into the blood of a healthy sheep. By long and tedious experiments, he proved that sheep, cattle, and horses could be made immune from the disease by vaccination.

Many scientists of the world doubted Pasteur's ability to make stock immune against anthrax. But in June, 1882, he demonstrated publicly at Pouilly le Fort his ability to treat animals with vaccine so that they would not fall victims to the germs of anthrax. He thus saved his country millions of dollars' worth of live stock in the years that followed.

A new disease was now attacking the chickens of Europe. Hens fell sick and dropped dead in a very brief time. A microbe was attacking the poultry which was unlike the microbe that had attacked the horses, cattle and sheep. Pasteur began a search for the microbe and found it. He experimented until he discovered how to prepare a vaccine which would save the chickens from the ravages of the disease.

While working on other microbes he was also studying the microbe which caused swine fever, a disease known as "rouget." In the United States alone in 1879 more than a million hogs died of this disease. In our country it is called hog cholera. Hog cholera serum, which is used so successfully throughout our country today is traceable directly to the work of Louis Pasteur. Billions of dollars' worth of hogs have been saved to the farmers throughout the world because of the work of this famous scientist.

Among the many researches made in his laboratory was one on hydrophobia. Pasteur was deeply concerned about this terrible affliction. In 1880, a report was made to him of a child, five years of age, who had been bitten in the face by a mad dog. The little fellow developed hydrophobia and died in intense suffering, at the end of twenty-four hours. Pasteur gathered some of the mucous four hours after the child's death, and mixed it with water; he then inoculated some rabbits with this and they died in less than thirty-six hours. Their saliva, injected into other rabbits, provoked an almost equally rapid death.

Pasteur was not convinced that the hydrophobia germ was contained alone in the saliva. He knew the saliva contained poisonous germs because a mad dog would bite into anything clean or unclean and thus the saliva could be poisoned by outside germs.

One day, Pasteur had his assistants drag a mad dog from its cage and hold it while he drew some saliva into a glass tube for testing purposes. The results of the test showed that the saliva was not a sure agent of hydrophobia. He thus found it necessary to seek further for the source of the germ.

He studied many cases with the deepest interest and at last he discovered, after making scientific tests, that the chief medium for the germ was in the brain. Today, when a dog is suspected of being mad, his head is sent to the laboratory for examination.

Pasteur studied how to weaken the germ in order that he might make people immune to the disease. He did this by removing a portion of a mad dog's brain and leaving it suspended in a tight vessel until it became dry, when the germs would be less virulent. He then used small portions of it mixed in water, to inoculate (by slow degrees) healthy dogs, until they were entirely free from an attack of the disease.

In a letter he wrote: "I have not dared to treat human beings after bites from rabid dogs; but the time is not far off, and I am much inclined to begin on myself—inoculating myself with rabies, and then arresting the consequences; for I am beginning to feel very sure of my results."

Mrs. Pasteur wrote to her children: "Your father is absorbed in his thoughts, talks little, sleeps little, rises at dawn, and, in one word, continues the life I began with him this day thirty-five years ago."

At this time, when Pasteur felt sure he could protect human beings from the rabies, little Joseph Meister, a boy nine years old, was bitten by a mad dog and brought to Pasteur. The furious dog had thrown the lad to the ground and bitten him fourteen times. Pasteur was worried. He knew the boy would die if not treated. He feared that some mistake might be made if he tried to inoculate him. After council with friends, he decided to try the remedy. The result was that the boy was completely cured and sent home well and happy.

The results of the inoculation on little

Joseph Meister proved to Pasteur that he had discovered a perfect method of protection against that terrible disease. Soon after this famous experiment four children in New York were bitten by a mad dog. The New York Herald solicited subscriptions for money to send the children, whose parents were poor, with the mother of the youngest one to France to see Pasteur. The children were all cured and sent back to America as well as ever.

A mother in France wrote to Pasteur: "You have done all the good a man could do on earth. If you will, you can surely find a remedy for the horrible disease called diphtheria. Our children, to whom we teach your name as that of a great benefactor, will owe their lives to you."—A mother.

Pasteur's health and strength were now fast failing, but in spite of his condition he took an active interest in the experiments on diphtheria, which were being made in his laboratories by his assistants. The serum treatment for diphtheria was discovered by M. Roux, one of Pasteur's students. Pasteur lived to see the fruits of this discovery and he was proud of his pupil whom he had taught: "Never to make a claim of a discovery until all possible doubt had been removed."

Before Pasteur's time many contagious diseases ravaged the nations of the world. Yellow fever, cholera, and bubonic plague or black death killed millions of people.

In London 100,000 people died of black death; 50,000 in Paris, and 60,000 in Florence. Whole families were wiped out. Villages were stricken until often there were not enough well people to care for the sick and bury the dead. Pasteur's discoveries have made it possible to control most of the contagious diseases. His science has revolutionized sanitation and disease-prevention methods.

Pasteur considered that a man's life is worthless if not useful to others. It is said of him: "He was a devoted friend to all men who were earnestly seeking the truth. He loved the heroes who had worked for humanity and passed on to the Great

Beyond. Neither jealousy, suspicion, nor carping criticism, ever cast a shadow over his life."

Pasteur once said: "Blessed is he who carries within himself an ideal, and who obeys it; an ideal of art, an ideal of science, an ideal of Gospel virtues. Therein lie the springs of great thoughts and great actions. They all reflect light from the infinite."

Every civilized nation on earth honored the name Pasteur. Someone has said: "To no one has it ever been given to accomplish work of such great importance for the well being of humanity. His memory will ever be cherished in the heart of a grateful world. He was the most perfect man who ever entered the Kingdom of Science."

THINKING IT THROUGH

1. What do you think of Pasteur's statement about "Will, Work and Success"? Name four great men whose lives illustrate this statement.
2. Tell in your own words the meaning of the couplet which the author says Pasteur's life calls to our minds.
3. Pasteur advised his pupil, "Never make a claim of a discovery until all possible doubt has been removed." Do you approve of this advice? Why?
4. Discuss the paragraph beginning, "Blessed is he who carries within himself an ideal."
5. What kind of a life did Pasteur regard as useless?
6. Can we estimate Pasteur's services to the world in dollars and cents?
7. Tell in your own words the story of Pasteur's work against the dread disease, hydrophobia.
8. Horace Mann once said: "Be ashamed to die until you have achieved some victory for mankind." How does this apply to Pasteur?

WORK

—L. M. Alcott

I am glad a task to me is given
    To labor day by day;
For it brings me health, and strength, and hope,
    And I cheerfully learn to say,
"Head, you may think; Heart, you may feel,
    But Hand, you should work always."

What is the object of work? The chief object of work is self-support. Nearly everyone must work in order to live. Boys and girls at school are living upon the labor of their parents. In many cases your parents are poor and are working very hard, early and late, to earn the money to keep you in school. Often they do without things that they would like to have in order to clothe you, board you, and buy your books. They do this gladly as they look forward with hope and pride to the day when you will be able to earn an honest living.

How can you ever repay such unselfish love? Let me tell you. By work, whole-souled work—doing the very best you can every single day. Have an aim. Go into training for some trade, business, or profession so that when you have completed your school course you may hold your head high among independent, self-supporting men. This is a duty you owe to yourselves and to your parents.

Every girl, as well as every boy, should have special training in some line of work, so that she may be able to support herself, if necessary. If a girl is needed at home, that is the place for her, but she should know how to make the home more pleasant by her presence, and she should learn how to assist her mother intelligently.

"Just a job or a golden chance?" — this question demands an answer every day
of your life. Will you go on as you have in the past,
or will you make today's tasks stepping stones to the success of tomorrow?
Successful men and women have a greater goal in view as they do each day's work.
They struggle hard against all difficulties to make tomorrow better than today.
This is how you, too, can become a success. As you do your tasks each day,
ask yourself, "Is it just a job, or is it a golden chance?"

JUST A JOB

—Edgar A. Guest

Is it just a job that is yours to hold,
A task that offers you so much gold,
Just so much work that is yours to do,
With never a greater goal in view?
What do you see, at your desk or loom,
Or the spot you fill in life's busy room,
Merely a flickering lamp that burns
With a sickly light as the mill-wheel turns,
And the same old grind in the same old ways,
With all the tomorrows like yesterdays?

Is it just a job, just a task to do,
So many pieces to build anew?
So many figures to add, and then,
Home for awhile and back again?
Are you just a clerk in a gaudy shop,
Pleased when a customer fails to stop,
Finding no joy in the things you sell,
Suddenly waiting for the quitting-bell?
Are your thoughts confined to the narrow space
And the dreariness of your present place?

Is it just a job, or a golden chance?
The first grim post of a fine advance,
The starting place on the road which leads
To the better joys and the bigger deeds?
Do your thoughts go out to the days to be,
Can your eyes look over the drudgery
And see in the distance the splendid flow
Of the broader life that you, too, may know?
What is your view of your circumstance:
Is it just a job or a golden chance?

During the Crimean War, an English cavalry brigade,
through someone's mistake, was ordered to charge a Russian battery
and silence its guns. To reach this battery the English horsemen had to cross a wide
plain, swept by steady gunfire from the battery.
Six hundred and thirty horsemen obeyed that terrible
order without question or hesitation, although they knew that they
faced certain death in that storm of shot and shell. Only one hundred and fifty returned
after the famous charge.
No one will ever know who was responsible for this costly blunder as Captain
Nolan, who gave the command: "Charge for the guns!" was the first man to fall as
he led his brigade to the charge.
This cavalry charge, which played only an unimportant part in the war,
was made famous by this poem. In it Tennyson built a monument in verse to the
heroic obedience of these soldiers.

THE CHARGE OF THE LIGHT BRIGADE

—Alfred Tennyson

Half a league, half a *league,*
Half a league onward,
All in the valley of Death
    Rode the six hundred.
"Forward, the Light *Brigade!*
Charge for the guns!" he said;
Into the valley of Death
    Rode the six hundred!

"Forward, the Light Brigade!"
    Was there a man *dismayed?*
Not though the soldiers knew
    Some one had *blundered;*
Theirs not to make reply,
Theirs not to reason why,
Theirs but to do and die.
Into the valley of Death
    Rode the six hundred.

Cannon to right of them,
Cannon to left of them,
Cannon in front of them
    Volleyed and thundered;
Stormed at with shot and shell,
Boldly they rode and well;
Into the jaws of Death,
Into the mouth of Hell,
    Rode the six hundred!

Flashed all their *sabers* bare,
Flashed as they turned in air,
Sabering the gunners there,
Charging an army, while
    All the world wondered;
Plunged in the battery-smoke,
Right through the line they broke:
Cossack and Russian
Reeled from the saber stroke,
    Shattered and *sundered*.
Then they rode back—but not,
    Not the six hundred.

Cannon to right of them,
Cannon to left of them,
Cannon behind them,
    Volleyed and thundered.
Stormed at with shot and shell,
While horse and hero fell,
They that had fought so well,
Came through the jaws of Death,
Back from the mouth of Hell,
All that was left of them,
    Left of six hundred.

When can their glory fade?
O, the wild charge they made!
    All the world wondered,
Honor the charge they made!
Honor the Light Brigade,
    Noble six hundred!

blundered — a gross error made through ignorance, confusion or careless
brigade — a large body of troops
Cossack — member of a favored Russian military caste
dismayed — without courage
league — distance from about 2.4 to 4.6 statute miles
sabers — cavalry swords
sundered — severed; cut in two
volleyed — simultaneous discharge of weapons

A BOY'S PRAYER

William DeWitt Hyde

Give me clean hands,
    clean words,
       and clean thoughts.

Help me to stand for the hard right
    against the easy wrong.

Save me from habits that harm.

Teach me to work as hard
    and play as fair in Thy sight alone
    as if all the world saw.

Forgive me when I am unkind,
    and help me to forgive those
    who are unkind to me.

Keep me ready to help others
    at some cost to myself.

> The door to the room of success swings on
> the hinges of opposition.
>
> —Bob Jones, Sr.

A committee was appointed by the Continental Congress to draft the
Declaration of Independence. The members of the committee were
Thomas Jefferson, John Adams, Benjamin Franklin, Roger Sherman,
Robert L. R. Livingston. Jefferson and Franklin were appointed as a subcommittee to
prepare the Declaration of Independence, but it fell to Jefferson to do the actual writing
of the document. Only a few changes were made in this draft
either by the Committee or by the Continental Congress.
After Jefferson read the Declaration aloud, Franklin said,
"That's good, Thomas! I wish I had done it myself."
When submitted for a vote, it was adopted by the narrow margin of only one vote.
The Declaration went forth signed by John Hancock,
the president of the Continental Congress.
As Hancock wrote his name in large, clear letters, he said, "There, John Bull can read
that without spectacles, and may now double his reward of five hundred pounds
for my head." Then turning, he added, "Gentlemen, we must all hang together."
"Yes," replied Benjamin Franklin, "or we shall all hang separately."
Later the other fifty-five members of the Continental Congress
signed the document. This selection tells of the lives of these great men.

SIGNERS OF THE DECLARATION OF INDEPENDENCE

—Frances Margaret Fox

We all know that Thomas Jefferson wrote the Declaration of Independence. When he knew that he had been chosen for the honor, he ordered a desk made by a carpenter, which must have been placed on a table because it was only fourteen inches long, ten inches wide, and three inches high. On this desk he did his writing of the Declaration. Finally, when the necessary changes were made, Jefferson penned what he refers to as a "fair copy," and it was this copy which John Hancock, as President of the Congress, ordered to be engrossed on parchment, to which, at peril of their lives, the fifty-six brave men signed their names.

School children who are taken to see the Declaration of Independence in the Library of Congress are always delighted when they see John Hancock's signature; always one in the group will remind the others that John Hancock said as he wrote his name, "There, John Bull can read that without spectacles!"

John Hancock

One signature which sometimes attracts attention is the tremblingly written name of Stephen Hopkins, of Rhode Island. Those who do not know the reason for the unsteady pen often suggest that this signer surely feared the gallows. Far from it! Stephen Hopkins, ship-builder, merchant, lawyer, and colonial governor of Rhode Island, was one of the bravest men who ever lived. Usually his secretary did his writing because he was afflicted with a disease known as "shaking palsy." When he signed the Declaration, he held his right wrist with his left hand and did his best to write his name plainly. He said, "If my hand does tremble, John Bull will find that my heart won't."

Step Hopkins

Saml Adams

As for Samuel Adams, when General Gage advised him to make peace with King George, this patriot firmly replied, "I trust I have long since made my peace with the King of kings. No personal considerations shall *induce* me to *abandon* the righteous cause of my country."

No wonder these men were long ago called "The Immortal Fifty-Six."

Josiah Bartlett

After John Hancock, Dr. Josiah Bartlett, of New Hampshire, was the next to sign the Declaration. History says he was the first to vote for it. He was one of the three "self-made men" of the fifty-six. It is a noteworthy fact that these leaders of men were, with the exception of three, all given the best education possible. Eight were Harvard graduates. Four graduated from Yale and four from Princeton. The college of William and Mary graduated three, while six were educated in England and Scotland. Several of the signers were given private tuition, "as high and costly as given at any university in the world."

Two of the signers became Presidents of the United States and two Vice-Presidents. To quote an additional bit of truth regarding the fifty-six, "Of those who survived the Revolutionary War, scarcely a man but was elected senator, congressman, supreme judge, governor, or President."

John Hart

Of the ten who died before the close of the war, John Hart's story is the saddest. All of the signers suffered deeply "in mind, body or estate," because of what they did for us when they signed that immortal roll; but John Hart was actually hunted for years through the swamps and woods of New Jersey by Tories who were determined upon his capture. The British did capture Captain Richard Stockton. They put him in jail in New York City and treated him so badly that he soon died.

induce — cause
abandon — forsake

Button Gwinnett

Button Gwinnett is the queer name of a rather unusual man who arrived in our country in 1770. He was a young Englishman of great wealth who immediately joined the colonies in their struggle for freedom. At the time of the adoption of the Declaration of Independence he was in Philadelphia attending the Congress as a delegate from Georgia. Unfortunately the very next year he and General McIntosh had a quarrel and fought a duel in which he was mortally wounded. Robert Morris was also born in England, as we know. From Scotland came James Wilson and John Witherspoon. Ireland sent us James Smith, George Taylor, and Matthew Thornton, while Francis Lewis came from Wales. Here then were eight fine gentlemen straight from the realm of King George, glad to sign our Declaration of Independence.

James Wilson
Geo. Taylor *Jas. Smith*
Matthew Thornton
Jno Witherspoon

John Witherspoon was the only clergyman numbered with the signers of the Declaration. He was fifty-four years old that July day, in 1776, so he knew what he was doing. He was a member of the War Board. They tell us that he often visited the troops and continually used his influence to make conditions easier for them. He became a college president after the war and wrote many religious books.

Rob Morris

Every school history tells something of the story of Robert Morris, the noble patriot who loaned his great fortune to the Continental Congress and made it possible for George Washington to compel Lord Cornwallis to surrender. For eight years Robert Morris managed the financial affairs of our country. Then when Robert Morris was an old man, at a time when our Government might have saved him by

paying back a little of the money which was his *due,* the creditors of this great man put him in a debtor's prison. No wonder he died soon!

Fran! Lewis

The patriot from Wales, who was a wealthy merchant, not only lost all his property which was taken by the British, but both he and his wife were kept in prison until what King George wished to have done didn't make any particular difference in the United States of America! Francis Lewis, from Wales, was ninety years old when he died.

Lewis Morris

When Lewis Morris signed the Declaration of Independence he well knew what was in store for him. This gentleman owned an estate of three thousand acres of the finest lands. He called his place Morrisania. There, with abundant wealth he lived like a prince. Although British troops were stationed near him and watched his every move, Lewis Morris signed the Declaration of Independence. Straightway he lost all his earthly possessions. Worst of all, his family were driven from their beautiful home as an example to all rebels. His descendants might be living at Morrisania to this day if Lewis Morris had not written his name in so *conspicuous* a place.

Arthur Middleton

Consider for a minute Arthur Middleton. His property also was *confiscated* and he suffered imprisonment which caused his death before the close of the war. Yet, as an individual who gave his all for his country, it cannot be said that his memory is *sufficiently honored.* Arthur Middleton was as true a patriot as John Hancock himself.

due — moral right
conspicuous — noticeable
confiscated — seized
sufficiently honored — honored enough

Th. Nelson jr.

Virginians should never forget Thomas Nelson, although to remember in detail all that befell him is far from pleasant. He saved Virginia from bankruptcy by turning his large fortune into the public treasury. At Yorktown, where he was in command of the State militia, he ordered the destruction of his own house because it seemed necessary to do so that victory might be ours.

This man, who loaned his money to the State that the soldiers of Virginia might be paid and so continue to fight the battles of the American Revolution, died at the age of fifty-one as one of the results of his generous patriotism. The *remnants* of his property were sold to pay his debts. When he signed the Declaration of Independence, he lost everything of value except the comfort of an approving conscience.

Francis Lightfoot Lee
Richard Henry Lee

The two Lees who signed the Declaration were wonderful men. As doubtless we all know, Francis Lightfoot Lee was one of Washington's dearest friends. He was a practical gentleman, and when the peace terms were agreed upon, it was Francis Lightfoot Lee who insisted that the United States should have the right to navigate the Mississippi and to fish on Newfoundland shores.

John Morton

The first of the signers to die was a Philadelphia judge, John Morton, whose death occurred in April, 1777. Many of his oldest and dearest friends had turned against him because he had signed the Declaration of Independence instead of making peace with the king; and so bitter were they, they refused to be *reconciled* to Judge Morton even on his death bed. The judge was ill only a few days, and almost with his last breath he spoke these words as his dying message to these old-time friends, "Tell them that they will live to see the hour when they shall *acknowledge* it to have been the most glorious service that I have ever rendered to my country."

Thomas Lynch Junr.

It is rather surprising that only two of the fifty-six signers met violent deaths, when every one of them considered such an exit from earth highly probable. Button Gwinnet was killed in a duel and Thomas Lynch, Jr., was drowned at sea.

When the latter, a highly educated man from South Carolina, accepted a commission as captain in the Revolutionary Army, his father insisted that he should not have accepted so low a commission. The son answered, "My present command is fully equal to my experience."

It was the father who was first sent as a delegate to the Continental Congress. He was taken dangerously ill. Thomas begged his superior officer for permission to visit his father but was refused. Fortunately the young man was then sent to Congress from his own State to take the father's place. The father died in his son's arms at Annapolis while trying to reach his home in South Carolina.

Not long after Thomas Lynch signed the Declaration of Independence and was gaining a reputation as a statesman, he was taken ill, and in 1779 was sent by his physicians on a sea voyage in the hope of benefiting his health. It is believed that his ship went down in a tempest and was lost with all on board.

Benj. a Franklin
Phil. Livingston

It is rather interesting to learn something of the ages of the men when they signed the Declaration of Independence. Benjamin Franklin, who leads the list of the five oldest, was seventy. Stephen Hopkins was sixty-nine, John Hart was sixty-eight, Francis Lewis was sixty-three, Matthew Thornton was sixty-two, and Philip Livingston was sixty.

Edward Rutledge.
Thos. Heyward Junr.

remnants — remainder
reconciled — restored to friendship
acknowledge — admit

Benjamin Rush

Elbridge Gerry

Th Jefferson

Thos. Stone

Thomas Lynch, who took his father's place, and Edward Rutledge were only twenty-seven, Thomas Heyward was thirty, Benjamin Rush was thirty-one, Elbridge Gerry was thirty-two, while Thomas Jefferson, Thomas Stone, and Arthur Middleton were thirty-three.

Charles Carroll of Carrollton

Charles Carroll, of Carrollton, is the gentleman who outlived all other signers of the Declaration. On the fourteenth of November, 1832, he died a short time before his ninety-sixth birthday.

It is recorded as a singular fact that twenty-four of the signers, nearly one-half, lived to the age of seventy or over. Fourteen lived on until eighty and no less than five to be ninety or more.

Twenty-four of these gentlemen were lawyers, fourteen were farmers, nine were merchants, four were physicians, and although four were educated for the ministry, only one was a clergyman on July 4, 1776, and only one was a manufacturer.

John Sanderson, author of Biographies of the Signers, and those who in several volumes completed the work he began, are the best authorities on the subject of the Declaration of Independence. After a somewhat extensive reading of those biographies, one outstanding fact is noticeable—these men went to their graves with their minds crystal clear.

In an article about the signers of the Declaration of Independence written by Loosing, which may be found in Harper's Magazine for the year 1858, we find these words:

"It is a fact worthy of record that the fifty-six members of the Continental Congress of 1776, who signed the Declaration of Independence and thereby took a position of great eminence in the sight of the nations, not one fell from his proud estate, either by the effects of political *apostasy* or lukewarmness or by moral *degradation.* In public and private life they remained pure; and in that glorious constellation of which the patriot of Monticello is the chief luminary, there is not a single star whose light is dim or unworthy of the highest *homage* that may be paid to man by the patriot and Christian."

apostasy — change of belief
degradation — corruption
homage — honor

THINKING IT THROUGH

These men courageously signed the Declaration of Independence even though they knew their lives and property would be in danger.

1. Name the outstanding qualities you found in the lives of "The Immortal Fifty-Six."
2. Do you think these characteristics are needed today?
3. When do you think a person should begin to build a strong character?
4. How have your attitudes changed after reading about men who have made great sacrifices for our country?
5. Can you now help others appreciate their sacrifice? How?

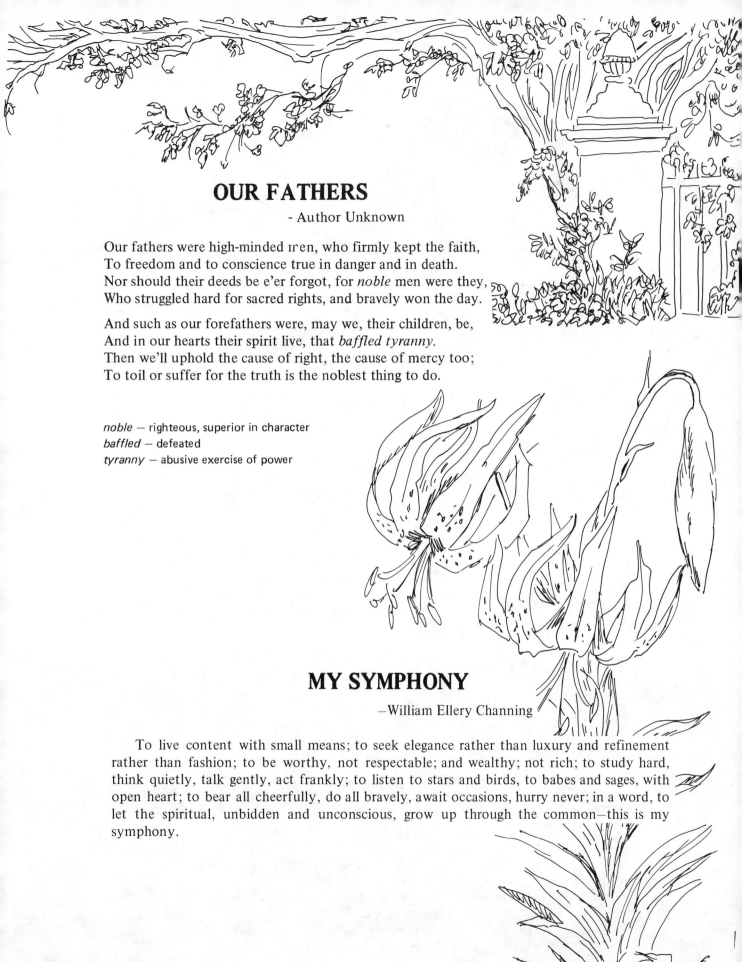

OUR FATHERS

- Author Unknown

Our fathers were high-minded ıren, who firmly kept the faith,
To freedom and to conscience true in danger and in death.
Nor should their deeds be e'er forgot, for *noble* men were they,
Who struggled hard for sacred rights, and bravely won the day.

And such as our forefathers were, may we, their children, be,
And in our hearts their spirit live, that *baffled tyranny*.
Then we'll uphold the cause of right, the cause of mercy too;
To toil or suffer for the truth is the noblest thing to do.

noble — righteous, superior in character
baffled — defeated
tyranny — abusive exercise of power

MY SYMPHONY

—William Ellery Channing

To live content with small means; to seek elegance rather than luxury and refinement rather than fashion; to be worthy, not respectable; and wealthy; not rich; to study hard, think quietly, talk gently, act frankly; to listen to stars and birds, to babes and sages, with open heart; to bear all cheerfully, do all bravely, await occasions, hurry never; in a word, to let the spiritual, unbidden and unconscious, grow up through the common—this is my symphony.

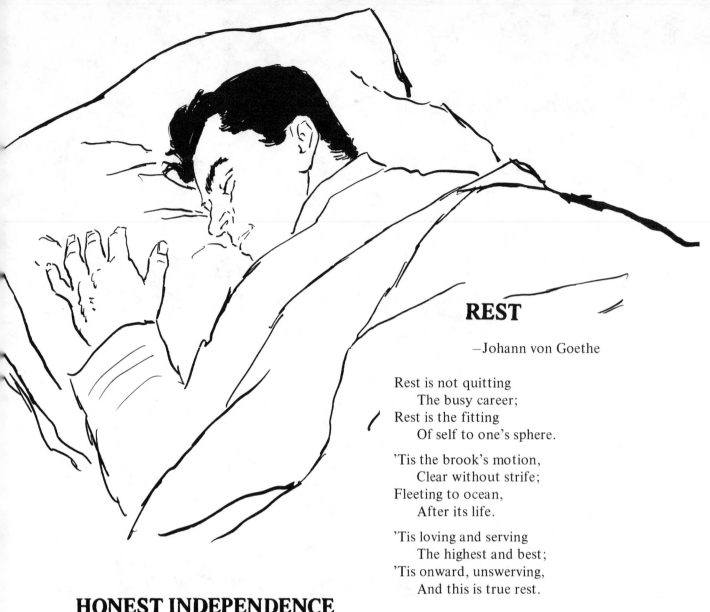

REST

—Johann von Goethe

Rest is not quitting
    The busy career;
Rest is the fitting
    Of self to one's sphere.

'Tis the brook's motion,
    Clear without strife;
Fleeting to ocean,
    After its life.

'Tis loving and serving
    The highest and best;
'Tis onward, unswerving,
    And this is true rest.

HONEST INDEPENDENCE

—Sir Henry Wotton

How happy is he born and taught
    Who serveth not another's will;
Whose armor is his honest thought,
    And simple truth his utmost skill.

LIFE

—Philip James Bailey

We live in deeds, not years; in thoughts, not breaths;
In feelings, not in figures on a dial.
We should count time by heart-throbs. He most lives
Who thinks most, feels the noblest, and acts the best.

THE ALAMO

In the 1830's and 1840's, the state of Texas was owned and held by Mexico, under the bloody and brutal rule of Santa Anna, president of Mexico. He was a very able, but cruel and treacherous leader. He hated the American colonists and ruled them like a tyrant. These Americans were as fine and brave a people as ever lived, and their fight for liberty forms one of the brightest pages of American history.

During the Texan War for Independence, Santa Anna, with a well-equipped army of more than 5,000 men, surrounded about 140 Texans in an old mission in San Antonio, Texas. For days the brave Texans held off the hordes of Mexicans, but one by one they were killed to the very last man. The defenders of the Alamo could have escaped, but they chose to stay and fight to the death. The fight that ensued has no equal in history for sheer heroism. Here died the gallant Colonel Travis, Colonel Bonham, James Bowie, David Crockett, and in all about 140 heroes such as the world has rarely seen. In this story, Ned Fulton is Santa Anna's prisoner.

THE FALL OF THE ALAMO
—Joseph A. Altsheler

The gray bar in the east broadened. A thin streak of shining silver cut through it, and touched for a moment the town, the river, the army, and the Alamo. Ned Fulton leaned against an edge of the earthwork, and breathed heavily and painfully. He had not known that his heart could beat so hard.

The same *portentous* silence prevailed everywhere. The men and women on the roofs of the houses were absolutely still. The calvary, their line now drawn completely about the mission, were motionless. Ned, straining his eyes toward the Alamo, could see nothing there. Suddenly he put up his hand and wiped his forehead. His fingers came away wet. His blood prickled in his veins like salt. He became impatient, angry. If the mine was ready, why did they not set the match? Such waiting was the pitch of cruelty.

"Cos, my brother," said Santa Anna to the *swart* general, "take your command. It was here that the Texan rebels humiliated you, and it is here that you shall have full vengeance."

Cos saluted, and strode away. He was to lead one of the attacking columns.

"Colonel Duque," said Santa Anna to another officer, "you are one of the bravest of the brave. You are to direct the attack on the northern wall, and may quick success go with you."

Duque glowed at the compliment, and he, too, strode away to the head of his column.

"Colonel Romera," said Santa Anna, "the third column is yours, and the fourth is yours, Colonel Morales. Take your places and, at the signal agreed, the four columns will charge with all their strength. Let us see which will be the first in the Alamo."

The two colonels saluted as the others had done, and joined their columns.

The bar of gray in the east was still broadening, but the sun itself did not yet show. The walls of the Alamo were still dim, and Ned could not see whether any

figures were there. Santa Anna had put a pair of powerful glasses to his eyes, but when he took them down he said nothing of what he had seen.

"Are all the columns provided?" he said to General Sesma, who stood beside him.

"They have everything," replied Sesma, "crowbars, axes, scaling ladders. Sir, they cannot fail!"

"No, they cannot," said Santa Anna *exultantly*. "These Texan rebels fight like demons, but we have now a net through which they cannot break. General Gaona, see that the bands are ready and direct them to play the Deguelo when the signal for the charge is given."

portentous — fateful
swart — dark complexioned

exultantly — rejoicingly

Ned shivered again. The "Deguelo" meant the "cutting-of-throats" and it, too, was to be the signal of no quarter. He remembered the red flag, and he looked up. It hung, as ever, on the tower of the church of San Fernando, and its scarlet folds moved slowly in the light morning breeze. General Gaona returned.

"The bands are ready, general," he said, "and when the signal is given they will play the *air* you have chosen."

A Mexican, trumpet in hand, was standing near. Santa Anna turned and said to him the single word:

"Blow!"

The man lifted the trumpet to his lips, and blew a long note that swelled to its fullest pitch, then died away in a soft echo.

It was the signal. A tremendous cry burst from the vast ring of the thousands, and it was taken up by the shrill voices of the women on the flat roofs of the houses. The great circle of cavalrymen shook their lances and sabers until they glittered.

When the last echo of the trumpet's dying note was gone the bands began to play with their utmost vigor the murderous tune that Santa Anna had chosen. Then four columns of picked Mexican troops, three thousand strong, rushed toward the Alamo. Santa Anna and the generals around him were tremendously excited. Their manner made no impression upon Ned then, but he recalled the fact afterward.

The boy became quickly unconscious of everything except the charge of the Mexicans and the Alamo. He no longer remembered anything about himself. The cruel throb of that murderous tune, the Deguelo, beat upon the drums of his ears, and mingled with it came the sound of the charging Mexicans, the beat of their feet, the clank of their arms, and the shouts of their officers.

Whatever may be said of the herded masses of the Mexican troops, the Mexican officers were full of courage. They were always in advance, waving their swords and shouting to their men to come on. Another silver gleam flashed through the gray light of the early morning, ran along the edges of swords and lances, and lingered for a moment over the dark walls of the Alamo.

No sound came from the mission, not a shot, not a cry. Were they asleep? Was it possible that every man, overpowered by *fatigue,* had fallen into slumber at such a moment? Could such as Crockett and Bowie and Travis be blind to their danger? Such painful questions raced through Ned's mind. He felt a chill run down his spine. Yet his breath was like fire to his lips.

"Nothing will stop them!" cried Santa Anna. "The Texans *cower* before such a splendid force! They will lay down their arms!"

Ned felt his body growing colder and colder, and there was a strange tingling at the roots of his hair. Now the people upon the roofs were shouting their utmost, and the voices of many women united in one shrill, piercing cry. But he never turned to look at them. His eyes were always on the charging host which *converged* so fast upon the Alamo.

air — tune

fatigue — weariness
cower — shake with fear
converged — moved together

The trumpet blew another signal, and there was a crash so loud that it made Ned jump. All the Mexican batteries had fired at once over the heads of their own troops at the Alamo. While the gunners reloaded the smoke of the discharge drifted away and the Alamo still stood silent. But over it yet hung a banner on which was written in great letters the word, "Texas."

PART II

The Mexican troops were coming close now. The bands playing the Deguelo swelled to greater volume, and the ground shook again as the Mexican artillery fired its second volley. When the smoke drifted away again, the Alamo itself suddenly burst into flame. The Texan cannon at close range poured their shot and shell into the dense ranks of the Mexicans. But piercing through the heavy thud of the cannon came the shriller and more deadly crackle of the rifles. The Texans were there, every one of them, on the walls. He might have known it. Nothing on earth could catch them asleep, nor could anything on earth or under it frighten them into laying down their arms.

Ned began to shout, but only hoarse cries came from a dry throat through dry lips. The great pulses in his throat were leaping again, and he was saying: "The Texans! The Texans! Oh, the brave Texans!"

But nobody heard him, Santa Anna, Filisola, Castrillon, Tolsa, Gaona and the other generals were leaning against the earthwork, absorbed in the tremendous spectacle that was passing before them. The soldiers who were to guard the prisoner forgot him and they, too, were *engrossed* in the terrible and thrilling panorama of war.

engrossed — completely occupied

Ned might have walked away, no one noticing, but he, too, had but one thought, and that was the Alamo.

He saw the Mexican columns shiver when the first volley was poured upon them from the walls. In a single glance aside he beheld the *exultant* look on the faces of Santa Anna and his generals die away, and he suddenly became conscious that the shrill shouting on the flat roofs of the houses had ceased. But the Mexican cannon still poured a cloud of shot and shell over the heads of their men at the Alamo, and the troops went on.

Ned, keen of ear and so intent that he missed nothing, could now separate the two fires. The crackle of the rifles which came from the Alamo *dominated.* Rapid, steady, *incessant,* it beat heavily upon the hearing and nerves. Pyramids and spires of smoke arose, drifted and arose again. In the *intervals* he saw the walls of the church a sheet of flame, and he saw the Mexicans falling by dozens and *scores* upon the plain. He knew that at short range the Texan rifles never missed, and that the hail of their bullets was cutting through the Mexican ranks like a fire through dry grass.

"How they fight!" he heard one of the generals—he never knew which—exclaim.

Then he saw the officers rushing about, shouting to the men, striking them with the flats of their swords and *urging* them on. The Mexican army responded to the appeal, lifted itself up and continued its rush. The fire from the Alamo seemed to Ned to increase. The fortress was a living flame. He had not thought that men could fire so fast, but they had three or four rifles apiece.

The silence which had replaced the shrill shouting in the town continued. All the crash was now in front of them, and where they stood the sound of the human voice would carry. In a dim far-away manner Ned heard the guards talking to one another. Their words showed uneasiness. It was not the swift triumphal rush into the Alamo that they had expected. Great *swaths* had been cut through the Mexican army. Santa Anna paled more than once when he saw his men falling so fast.

"They cannot recoil! They cannot!" he cried.

exultant — triumphant
dominated — excelled in skill and power
incessant — without stopping
intervals — pauses
one score — twenty

urging — forcing
swaths — paths

But they did. The column led by Colonel Duque, brave man, was now at the northern wall, and the men were rushing forward with the crowbars, axes, and scaling ladders. The Texan rifles, never more deadly, sent down a storm of bullets upon them.

Ned saw the face of Santa Anna turn purple with rage. He struck the earthwork furiously with the flat of his sword.

"Go! Go!" he cried to Gaona and Tolsa. "Rally them! See that they do not run!"

The two generals sprang from the battery and rushed to their task. The Mexican cannon had ceased firing, for fear of shooting down their own men, and the smoke was drifting away from the field. The morning was also growing much lighter. The gray dawn had turned to silver, and the sun's red rim was just showing above the eastern horizon.

The Texan cannon was silent, too. The rifles were now doing all the work. The volume of their fire never *diminished.* Ned saw the field covered with slain, and many wounded were drifting back to the shelter of the earthworks and the town.

Duque's column was *rallied,* but the column on the east and the column on the west were also driven back, and Santa Anna rushed messenger after messenger, hurrying up fresh men, still driving the whole Mexican army against the Alamo. He shouted orders incessantly, although he remained safe in the rear.

Ned felt an immense joy. He had seen the attack beaten off at three points. A force of twenty to one had been *compelled* to recoil. His heart swelled with pride in those friends of his. But they were so few in number! Even now the Mexican masses were reforming. The officers were among them, driving them forward with threats and blows. The great ring of Mexican cavalry, intended to keep any of the Texans from escaping, also closed in, driving their own infantry forward to the assault.

Ned's heart sank as the whole Mexican army, gathering now at the northern or lower wall, rushed straight at the barrier. But the deadly fire of the rifles flashed from it and their front line went down. Again they *recoiled,* and again the cavalry closed in, holding them to the task.

There was a pause of a few moments. The town had been silent for a long time, and the Mexican soldiers themselves ceased to shout. Clouds of smoke eddied and drifted about the buildings. The light of the morning, first gray, then silver, turned to gold. The sun, now high above the earth's rim, poured down a flood of rays.

Everything stood out sharp and clear. Ned saw the buildings of the Alamo dark against the sun, and he saw men on the walls. He saw the Mexican columns pressed together in one great force, and he even saw the still faces of many who lay silent on the plain.

He knew that the Mexicans were about to charge again, and his feeling of exultation passed. He no longer had hope that the defenders of the Alamo could beat back so many. He thought again how few, how very few, were the Texans.

PART III

The silence endured but a moment or two. Then the Mexicans rushed forward in a mighty mass at the low northern wall, the front lines firing as they went. Flame burst from the wall, and Ned heard once more the deadly crackle of the Texan rifles. The

recoiled — drew back

diminished — became less
rallied — aroused to action
compelled — forced

ground was littered by the trail of the Mexican fallen, but driven by their officers, they went on.

Ned saw them reach the wall and plant the scaling ladders, many of them. Scores of men swarmed up the ladders and over the wall. A heavy division forced its way into the *redoubt* through the *sally port*, and as Ned saw it he uttered a deep gasp. He knew that the Alamo was doomed. And the Mexicans knew it, too.

The shrill screaming of the women began again from the flat roofs of the houses, and shouts burst from the army also.

"We have them! We have them!" cried Santa Anna, exultant and excited.

Sheets of flame still burst from the Alamo, and the rifles still poured bullets on the swarming Mexican forces, but the *breach* had been made. The Mexicans went over the low wall in an unbroken stream, and they crowded through the sally port by hundreds. They were inside now, rushing with the *overwhelming* weight of twenty to one upon the little garrison. They seized the Texan guns, cutting down the gunners with lances and sabers, and they turned the captured cannon upon the defenders.

Some of the buildings inside the walls were of adobe, and they were soon shattered by the cannon balls. The Texans, covered with smoke and dust and the sweat of battle, were forced back by the press of numbers into the convent yard, and then into the church and hospital. Here the cannon and rifles in hundreds were turned upon them, but they still fought. Often, with no time to reload their rifles, they clubbed them, and drove back the Mexican rush.

The Alamo was a huge volcano of fire and smoke, of shouting and death. Those who looked on became silent again, *appalled* at the sights and sound. The smoke rose far above the mission, caught by a light wind drifted away to the east. The Mexican generals brought up fresh forces and drove them at the fortress. A heavy column, attacking on the south side, where no defenders were now left, poured over a stockade and crowded into the mission. The circle of cavalry about the Alamo again drew closer, lest any Texan should escape. But it was a useless precaution. None sought flight.

In very truth, the last hope of the Alamo was gone, and perhaps there was none among the defenders who did not know it. There were a few wild and desperate characters of the border, whom nothing in life became so much as their manner of leaving it. In the *culminating moment* of the great tragedy they bore themselves as well as the best.

Travis, the commander, and Bonham stood in the long room of the hospital with a little group around them, most of them wounded, the faces of all black with powder smoke. But they fought on. Whenever a Mexican appeared at the door an *unerring* rifle bullet struck him down. Fifty fell at that single spot before the rifles, yet they succeeded in dragging up a cannon, thrust its muzzle in at the door, and fired it twice, loaded with grape shot, into the room.

redoubt — stronghold
sally port — gate
breach — break
overwhelming — crushing

appalled — horrified
culminating moment — time of greatest danger
to the defenders of the Alamo
unerring — unfailing

The Texans were cut down by the shower of missiles, and the whole place was filled with smoke. Then the Mexicans rushed in and the few Texans who had survived the grape shot fell fighting to the last with their clubbed rifles. Here lay Travis of the white soul; beside him fell the brave Bonham, who had gone out for help, and who had returned to die with his comrades. The Texans who had defended the room against so many were only fifteen in number, and they were all silent now.

Now the whole attack converged on the church, the strongest part of the Alamo, where the Texans were making their last stand. The place was seething with fire and smoke, but above it still floated the banner upon which was written in great letters the word, "Texas."

The Mexicans, pressing forward in dense masses, poured in cannon balls and musket balls at every opening. Half the Texans were gone, but the others never ceased to fire with their rifles. Within that raging inferno they could hardly see one another for the smoke, but they were all animated by the same purpose, to fight to the death and to carry as many of their foes with them as they could.

Evans, who had commanded the cannon, rushed for the magazine to blow up the building. They had agreed that if all hope were lost he should do so, but he was killed on his way by a bullet, and the others went on with the combat.

Near the entrance to the church stood a great figure swinging a clubbed rifle. His raccoon skin cap was lost, and his eyes burned like coals of fire in his swarthy face. It was Crockett, gone mad with battle, and the Mexicans who pressed in recoiled before the deadly sweep of the clubbed rifle. Some were awed by the terrific figure, dripping blood, and wholly unconscious of danger.

"Forward!" cried a Mexican officer, and one of his men went down with a shattered skull. The others shrank back again, but a new figure pressed into the ring. It was that of the younger Urrea. At the last moment he had left the cavalry and joined in the assault.

"Don't come within reach of his blows!" he cried. "Shoot him! Shoot him!"

He snatched a double-barreled pistol from his own belt and fired twice straight at Crockett's breast. The great Tennesseean staggered, dropped his rifle, and the flame died from his eyes. With a howl of triumph his foes rushed upon him, plunged their swords and bayonets into his body, and he fell dead with a heap of the Mexican slain about him.

A bullet whistled past Urrea's face and killed a man beyond him. He sprang back. Bowie, still suffering severe injuries from a fall from a platform, was lying on a cot in the arched room to the left of the entrance. Unable to walk, he had received at his request two pistols, and now he was firing them as fast as he could pull the triggers and reload.

"Shoot him! Shoot him at once!" cried Urrea.

His own pistol was empty now, but a dozen musket balls were fired into the room. Bowie, hit twice, nevertheless raised himself upon his elbow, aimed a pistol with a clear eye and a steady hand, and pulled the trigger. A Mexican fell, shot through the heart, but another volley of musket balls was discharged at the Georgian. Struck in both head and heart he suddenly straightened out and lay still upon the cot. Thus died the famous Bowie.

Mrs. Dickinson and her baby had been hidden in the arched room on the other side for protection. The Mexicans killed a Texan named Walters at the entrance, and, wild with *ferocity*, raised his body upon a half dozen bayonets while the blood ran down in a dreadful stream upon those who held it aloft.

Urrea rushed into the room and found the cowering woman and her baby. The Mexicans followed, and were about to slay them, too, when a gallant figure rushed between. It was the brave and humane Almonte. Sword in hand, he faced the savage horde. He uttered words that made Urrea turn dark with shame and leave the room. The soldiers were glad to follow.

At the far end of the church a few Texans were left, still fighting with clubbed rifles. The Mexicans drew back a little, raised their muskets and fired an immense shattering volley. When the smoke cleared away not a single Texan was standing, and then the troops rushed in with sword and bayonet.

It was nine o'clock in the morning, and the Alamo had fallen. The defenders were only seven score, and they had died to the last man. A messenger rushed away at once to Santa Anna with the news of the triumph, and he came from the shelter, glorying, exulting and crying that he had destroyed the Texans.

Mrs. Dickinson — the only woman in the Alamo during the fight. She lived for many years in San Antonio after the battle.

ferocity — savagery

THE GLORY OF GOD IN CREATION

— Thomas Moore

Thou art, O God, the life and light
  Of all this wondrous world we see;
Its glow by day, its smile by night,
  Are but reflections caught from thee.
Where'er we turn, thy glories shine,
And all things fair and bright are thine.

When day, with farewell beam, delays
  Among the opening clouds of even,
And we can almost think we gaze
  Through opening *vistas* into heaven,
Those hues that make the sun's decline
So soft, so radiant, Lord, are thine.

When night, with wings of starry gloom,
  O'ershadows all the earth and skies,
Like some dark, beauteous bird, whose plume
  Is sparkling with unnumbered eyes,
That sacred gloom, those fires divine,
So grand, so countless, Lord, are thine.

When youthful Spring around us breathes,
  Thy spirit warms her fragrant sigh,
And every flower that Summer wreathes
  Is born beneath thy kindling eye:
Where'er we turn, thy glories shine,
And all things fair and bright are thine.

vistas — distant views

THINKING IT THROUGH

1. Give the meaning of the word "glory."
2. What does verse two describe? verse three?
3. What is the theme of this poem?

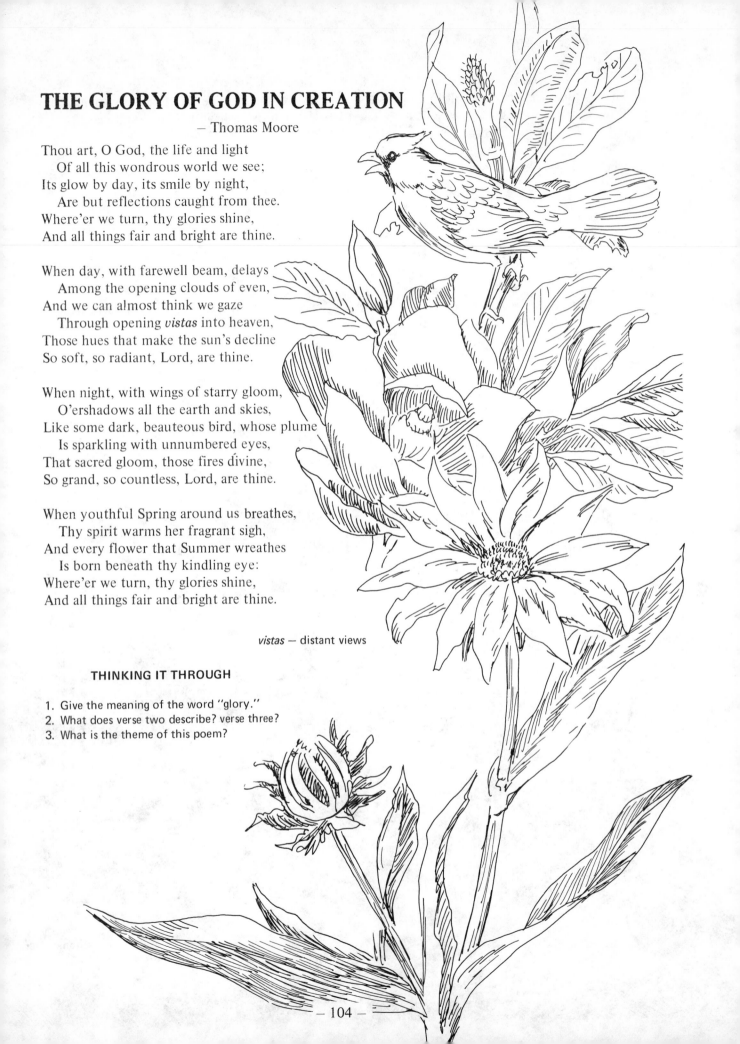

PSALM 8

O Lord our Lord, how excellent is thy name
in all the earth! who hast set thy glory
above the heavens.

Out of the mouth of babes and sucklings
hast thou ordained strength because of
thine enemies, that thou mightest still
the enemy and the avenger.

When I consider thy heavens, the work of
thy fingers, the moon and the stars, which
thou hast ordained;

What is man, that thou art mindful of him?
and the son of man, that thou visitest him?

For thou hast made him a little lower than
the angels, and hast crowned him with glory
and honour.

Thou madest him to have dominion over the
works of thy hands: thou hast put all
things under his feet:

All sheep and oxen, yea, and the beasts of
the field;

The fowl of the air, and the fish of the sea,
and whatsoever passeth through the paths of
the seas.

O Lord our Lord, how excellent is thy name
in all the earth!

Pioneers, whether founding a country, discovering a cure, or
creating better methods of doing necessary tasks, are invariably people who
have a goal, something specific they want to achieve.
Clara Barton, founder of the American Red Cross, was a pioneer who desired to achieve
the very best assistance for wounded soldiers. As you read this story,
notice that her desire to help those in need led her to forget her own shy nature
in courageous, dedicated service to others.

CLARA BARTON*

—Grace Humphrey

Clarissa Harlowe Barton was born on December 25, 1821, in an old farm-house in Worcester County, Massachusetts. Her grandfather had fought through the Revolution, and her father had been in Mad Anthony Wayne's campaigns against the Indians. Clara listened to many a stirring story of the dangers they had met. As they fought their battles over again, she learned her country's history and loved it passionately.

The older Barton children were her teachers, and very rapidly indeed she learned. For she went to school at three, able to spell many words of three syllables but so shy that she could not answer questions. Her athletic brother David, whom she admired greatly, taught her to ride.

"Learning to ride is just learning a horse," said he.

"How can I learn a horse?" asked the little sister.

"Just feel that the horse is part of yourself, the big half for the time being. Here, hold fast by the mane," and David lifted her up to a colt's back, sprang on another himself, and away they galloped down the pasture—a mad ride which they repeated often, till she learned to stick on. In after years when she rode strange horses in a trooper's saddle for all-night gallops to safety, she was grateful to David for those wild rides among the colts.

Strong in body, alert in mind, Clara Barton grew up, never free from shyness unless she was busily at work. "The only real fun is doing things," she would say. She helped milk and churn, and she learned to drive a nail straight.

When she was eleven, David was seriously injured by a fall from the roof of a new barn. For two years he was an invalid. At once Clara took charge of the sickroom. She changed from a lively child, fond of outdoor sports, to a nurse, calm and cheerful, no matter how exacting the doctors' orders were, no matter how much David was suffering. The sickroom was kept tidy and quiet. Clara was clear-headed and always at her post. Nothing was too hard for her to do well if it would make her brother more comfortable. During those two years she did not have even one half-holiday.

"That child's a born nurse," the neighbors would say. And the doctors, agreeing, praised her tenderness and patience. But these two years made her more sensitive and self-conscious. Her shyness made her a real problem to her mother.

"Give her some responsibility," advised a wise family friend; "give her a school to teach. For others she will be fearless."

Far ahead of girls of her age in her studies, at fifteen Clara Barton put up her hair and lengthened her skirts and went to face her forty pupils. "It was one of the most awful moments in my life," she said long afterwards. "I could not find my voice; my hand trembled so much that I was afraid to turn the page. But the end of the first day proved that I could do it."

Her pluck and strength won the respect of the big rough boys, who found that she was as sturdy as they. The school was a great success, and for sixteen years she taught, winter and summer.

In Bordentown, New Jersey, no school was possible, she heard, because the children ran wild on the streets. The town officials were convinced that no school could succeed there. Here was something to be done; it challenged her!

"Give me three months, and I'll teach for nothing," she proposed, her eyes flashing with determination.

In a tumble-down old building she began with six rough children from the streets, each of whom at the end of the day became an enthusiastic advertisement for the new teacher. At the close of the school year she had an assistant, because there were six hundred children on the rolls. A large new building was erected, the first public school in the state. For Clara Barton had a gift for teaching, as well as a spirit of enthusiasm.

When her voice gave out, she went to Washington for a rest and secured a position in the patent office. So she was at the capital when the conflict long threatening between North and South developed into war. Fort Sumter was fired on. The time for sacrifice had come.

In response to Lincoln's call for volunteers, Massachusetts sent men immediately. On the historic nineteenth of April one regiment was attacked in the streets of Baltimore by an angry crowd. With many wounded, their train finally reached Washington and was met by a number of sympathetic women, Clara Barton among

them. In the group of injured soldiers she recognized some of her old pupils and friends. At the infirmary she helped dress their wounds. Nothing was ready for such an emergency. Handkerchiefs gave out. Women rushed to their homes and tore up sheets for bandages.

This was Clara Barton's first experience in caring for wounded soldiers. She wanted them to have the necessities and all the comforts that were possible. So she put an advertisement in a Worcester paper, asking for supplies and money for the wounded men, and stating that she would give out whatever was sent. The response of Massachusetts was overwhelming. The food and clothing filled her apartment to overflowing, and she had to rent space in a warehouse.

This work made a new person of the shy Clara Barton who had been a bundle of fears. This was no time to be self-conscious. Here was a great need, and she knew that she had the ability to meet it.

South of Washington battles were going on. Transports left each day with provisions for the army of the Potomac, returning with a load of wounded soldiers. Clara Barton went to the docks to meet them. She moved about, bandaging here, giving medicine there, feeding those weak from lack of nourishment, and writing letters home. She was sick at heart when she saw men who had lain on the damp ground for hours with a fever, so that her dressings and tender care were too late.

If only wounds could be attended to as soon as the soldiers fell in battle, she realized, hundreds of deaths could be prevented. She must go to the front, to the very firing line, even though it was against all army regulations and against public sentiment. For many weeks she met only rebuffs and refusals, always the same reply: "No, the battlefield is no place for a woman. It is full of danger!"

True—but how great was the need of the men at the front! Help must be brought to them when they fell. When she laid her plan before her father, he said, "If you believe this is your duty, you must go to the front. You need not fear harm. Every true soldier will respect and bless you."

From that time on, she determined to keep trying until she received permission. At last she was able to put her request to General Rucker, asking him for a pass to the battle front. "I have the supplies. Give me a way to reach the men," she begged.

"You must think of the dangers this work will bring you. At any time you may be under the fire of guns."

"But I am the daughter of a soldier; I am not afraid of the battlefield." She described to him the condition of the men when they reached Washington and added earnestly, "I must go to the front to care for them quickly."

The passport was given her, and through the weary years of the war she stayed at her post—giving medicine to the sick, stimulants to the wounded and dying, nourishing food to men faint from loss of blood. Working under no society or leader, she was free to come and go. On sixteen battlefields, during the hot summer days of the siege of Charleston, all through the Wilderness Campaign, in the Richmond hospitals, there was no limit to her service. And from her first day on the firing-line she had the confidence of the officers and their help and encouragement. Wherever there were wounded soldiers who had been under her care, Clara Barton's name was spoken with affection.

In so far as was possible, she was told in advance about battles that were being planned, so that she might be ready with her supplies. At Antietam, while shot was falling around the group of workers, she ordered her wagons driven to an old farmhouse just back of the lines. Between the tall rows of corn, into the barnyard, the worst cases were carried. For lack of medical supplies the surgeons had been using bandages of corn husks.

Her supplies quickly unloaded, Clara Barton hurried out to revive the wounded, giving them bread soaked in wine. The supply of bread ran out; she had only three cases of wine left. "Open them," she commanded; "give us that, and God help us!" For faster and faster the wounded soldiers were coming in. She watched the men open the cases. What was that packed around the bottles? Corn-meal! It could not have been worth more if it had been gold-dust. In the farm-house they found kettles. She mixed the corn-meal with water and soon was making great quantities of gruel. All night long she helped carry this hot food up and down the rows of wounded soldiers.

On one of these trips she met a surgeon, tired and disheartened. He had only one short candle left, and if men's lives were to be saved, the doctors must work all night. "Heartless neglect and carelessness," he stormed. But Miss Barton had four boxes of candles in her stores, ready for just such an emergency.

Near that battlefield at Antietam she remained until all her supplies were gone. "If we had had more wagons," she reported to General Rucker, "we could have cared for all the wounded soldiers."

"You shall have enough the next time," he responded. And the government, recognizing the value of her service, gave her ten wagons with drivers and sixty mules.

When the drivers were rebellious and sulky because they were forced to serve under the orders of a woman, she controlled them just as she had controlled the rough boys in her New Jersey school. Once she prepared a hot dinner and asked them to share it. After she had cleared away the dishes, the men came up to her, awkward and self-conscious.

"Come and get warm," she welcomed them.

"No'm, we didn't come for that," said the leader. "We come to tell you we're ashamed. Truth is, lady, we didn't want to drive these wagons. We knew there was fightin' ahead for us to do, an' we never saw a train of wagons with a woman in charge before. Now, we've been mean and contrary all day long, and here you've treated us like a general and his staff. It's the best meal we've had in two years, and we shan't trouble you again."

The next morning they brought her a steaming hot breakfast. For six months they stayed with her, through battles and marches, through snow and heat, a devoted corps of assistants, always ready for her orders. They helped her nurse the sick and dress the wounded. And day by day they themselves grew kinder.

Once Clara Barton worked for five days and nights with only three hours of sleep. Often in danger, it seemed as though .she were protected by some special charm so that she might save the lives of others.

She gave her help to men who had fought on either side. They were suffering, and they needed her; that was enough. She went over to Fredericksburg, where every stone wall was a blazing line of battle. A regiment came marching down the road. She stepped aside. The general saw her and leaned from his saddle to say: "You're in great danger, madam. Do you want protection?"

"Thank you, but I think—" Clara Barton looked at the ranks of soldiers marching past—"I think, sir, I'm the best protected woman in the United States!"

"That's so, that's so!" cried out the men as they gave her a great cheer that was taken up by line after line until it sounded like the cheering after a victory.

"I believe you're right, madam," said the general, bowing low.

Over the battlefield a sharp wind was blowing. The suffering men lay shivering and half frozen in the bitter cold. Some were found famished under the snow. Clara Barton had all the wounded brought to one place and great fires built. But these fires did not give enough heat to warm them. What to do? She discovered an old chimney not far away. "Tear it down," she ordered; "heat the bricks and place them around the men." Soon she had kettles of coffee and gruel steaming over the fires, and thus saved many lives.

As the war drew to an end, President Lincoln received hundreds of letters from anxious parents asking for news of their boys. The list of missing totaled sixty thousand. In despair the President sent for Clara Barton, thinking she had more information than anyone else, and asked her to take up the task. A four-years' task it proved to be. She copied infirmary and burial lists. She studied records of prisons and hospitals. She succeeded in tracing and sending definite word about thirty thousand men. Through the whole country her name became a household word.

Her strong will had held her body to its work during the long war, and afterwards for the task of tracing missing men. Then the doctors insisted that she must rest and sent her to Switzerland for a change of scene. After a month, when she was beginning to feel some improvement, she had callers one day who represented the International Red Cross Society.

"What is that?" asked Clara Barton.

And they explained how a Swiss, visiting the battlefield of Solferino and seeing thousands of wounded soldiers poorly cared for, had planned a society for the relief of soldiers. Its badge, a red cross on a white ground, gave its workers protection from both armies. Red Cross workers helped all persons without regard to their race or religion or uniform. This was exactly the principle on which Clara Barton had been working, and today it is the very heart of the Red Cross plan. Already, these visitors said, twenty-two nations had formed such societies. But the United States, though invited twice, had done nothing. They asked her help.

Three days afterwards the Franco-Prussian War began, and soon Clara Barton was again at the front. With the German army she entered Strasbourg after the siege. On every hand were sick and wounded soldiers and homeless, starving women and children. There she helped the Red Cross Society in its relief work. And this work made her enthusiastic about the Red Cross. For at once she felt the difference. She saw the new society accomplish in four months, with system and trained workers, what our country had failed to do in four years. What a contrast! Wherever the white flag with the red cross was flying, there were supplies in plenty, prompt attention to wounds, cleanliness and comfort. Wherever she had worked alone, there were mistakes, delays, needless suffering, and lives sacrificed. She said to herself, "When I return to America, I will try to make our people understand what the Red Cross means."

She succeeded, though it was a task of years. She found officials hard to convince, clinging to the tradition that forbade any alliance with foreign countries.

But in March, 1882, the United States organized a Red Cross society. Clara Barton became the first president of the American Red Cross, an office she held for twenty-two years. It was her suggestion that the Red Cross be prepared to give relief in time of peace as well as war. Through her influence the International Red Cross Conference also adopted this American plan.

THINKING IT THROUGH

1. Name three words that you think describe Clara Barton.
2. How did her life benefit others? Was it worthwhile to give her life in this way? Why?
3. What personal rewards do you think she gained because of her unselfishness?
4. Name some ways in which you can serve others. Name some ways that you will strive to serve others today.
5. Give an example of an unselfish act you have done for others.

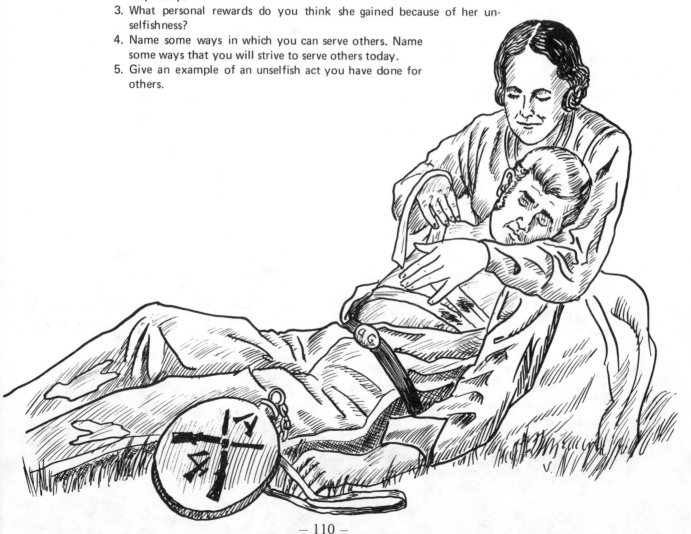

A PSALM OF LIFE

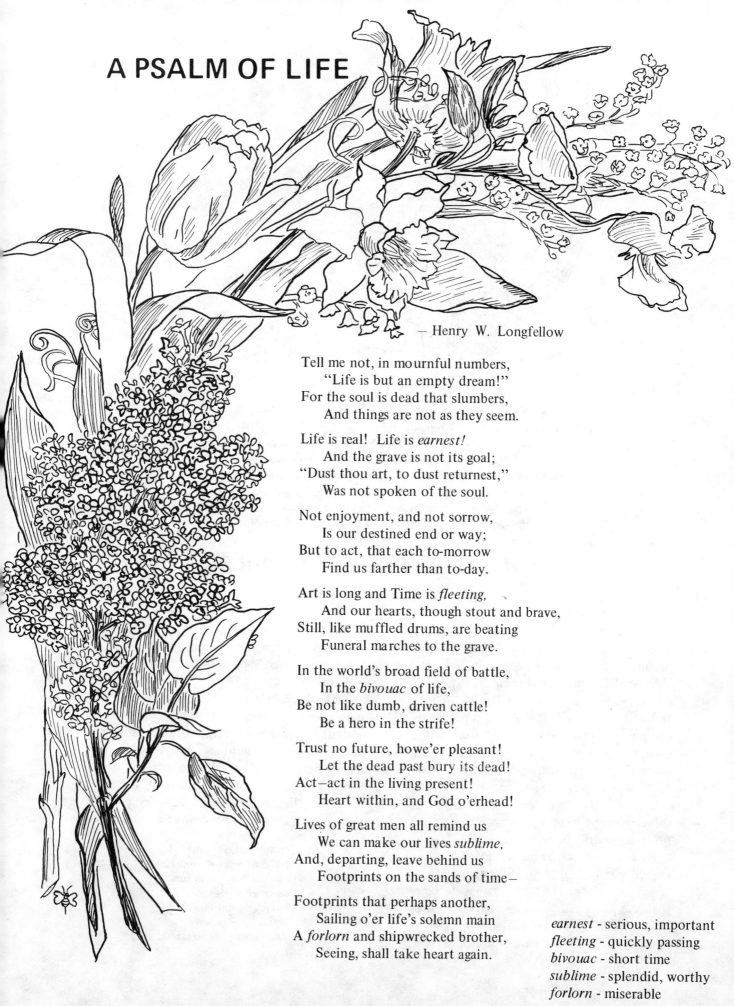

– Henry W. Longfellow

Tell me not, in mournful numbers,
    "Life is but an empty dream!"
For the soul is dead that slumbers,
    And things are not as they seem.

Life is real! Life is *earnest!*
    And the grave is not its goal;
"Dust thou art, to dust returnest,"
    Was not spoken of the soul.

Not enjoyment, and not sorrow,
    Is our destined end or way;
But to act, that each to-morrow
    Find us farther than to-day.

Art is long and Time is *fleeting,*
    And our hearts, though stout and brave,
Still, like muffled drums, are beating
    Funeral marches to the grave.

In the world's broad field of battle,
    In the *bivouac* of life,
Be not like dumb, driven cattle!
    Be a hero in the strife!

Trust no future, howe'er pleasant!
    Let the dead past bury its dead!
Act—act in the living present!
    Heart within, and God o'erhead!

Lives of great men all remind us
    We can make our lives *sublime,*
And, departing, leave behind us
    Footprints on the sands of time—

Footprints that perhaps another,
    Sailing o'er life's solemn main
A *forlorn* and shipwrecked brother,
    Seeing, shall take heart again.

earnest - serious, important
fleeting - quickly passing
bivouac - short time
sublime - splendid, worthy
forlorn - miserable

This selection is from a pamphlet called "The Crisis," published in 1776 by Thomas Paine. General Washington had lost the battle of Long Island and had been forced to retreat from New York toward Philadelphia. Many of Washington's soldiers who had enlisted for short terms were on the point of deserting or resigning at the end of their terms. In this serious situation Washington ordered "The Crisis" to be read before every company of soldiers in his army. As you read, find why Washington felt this message would stir his men to stay and fight for victory.

TIMES THAT TRY MEN'S SOULS

—Thomas Paine

These are the times that try men's souls. The summer soldier and the sunshine patriot will, in this *crisis*, shrink from the service of his country; but he that stands it now deserves the love and thanks of man and woman. *Tyranny*, like hell, is not easily conquered; yet we have this *consolation* with us, that the harder the conflict, the more glorious the triumph. What we obtain too cheap, we *esteem* too lightly; 'tis dearness only that gives everything its value. Heaven knows how to put a proper price upon its goods; it would be strange, indeed, if so *celestial* an article as freedom should not be highly rated. Britain, with an army to enforce her tyranny, has declared that she has a right, not only to tax, but to "bind us in all cases whatsoever," and if being bound in that manner is not slavery,

then is there not such a thing as slavery upon earth. Even the expression is *impious*, for so unlimited a power can belong only to God.

I have as little superstition in me as any man living, but my secret opinion has been, and still is, that God Almighty will not give up a people to military destruction, or leave them unsupportedly to perish, who have so *earnestly* and so repeatedly sought to avoid the *calamities* of war, by every decent method which wisdom could invent.

crisis — crucial time
tyranny — cruel, oppressive government
consolation — comfort
celestial — heavenly
impious — profane
earnestly — gravely
calamities — disasters

I once felt all that kind of anger which a man ought to feel, against the mean principles that are held by the Tories; a noted one, who kept a tavern at Amboy, was standing at his door, with as pretty a child in his hand, about eight or nine years old, as I ever saw, and after speaking his mind as freely as he thought was prudent, finished with this unfatherly expression, "Well! give me peace in my day." Not a man lives on the continent but fully believes that a separation must some time or other finally take place, and a generous parent should have said, "If there must be trouble, let it be in my day, that my child may have peace"; and his single reflection, well applied, is sufficient to awaken every man to duty. Not a place upon earth might be so happy as America. Her situation is *remote* from all the wrangling world, and she has nothing to do but to trade with them. A man can distinguish in himself between temper and principle, and I am as confident as I am that God governs the world, that America will never be happy till she gets clear of foreign *dominion*. Wars without ceasing will break out till that period arrives, and the continent must in the end be conqueror; for though the flame of liberty may sometimes cease to shine, the coal can never *expire*.

remote — distant
dominion — authority
expire — die

The heart that feels not now is dead; the blood of his children will curse his cowardice who shrinks back at a time when a little might have saved the whole, and made them happy. I love the man that can smile in trouble, that can gather strength from distress, and grow brave by reflection. 'Tis the business of little minds to shrink; but he whose heart is firm, and whose conscience approves his conduct, will *pursue* his principles unto death. My own line of reasoning is to myself as straight and clear as a ray of light. Not all the treasures of the world, so far as I believe, could have *induced* me to support an *offensive* war, for I think it murder; but if a thief breaks into my house, burns and destroys my property, and kills or threatens to kill me or those that are in it, and to "bind me in all cases whatsoever" to his absolute will, am I to suffer it? What *signifies* it to me, whether he who does it is a king or a common man; my countryman or not my countryman; whether it be done by an individual *villain* or an army of them? If we reason to the root of things we shall find no differences; neither can any just cause be assigned why we should punish in the one case and pardon in the other.

pursue — practice
induced — caused
offensive — attacking
signifies — matters
villian — scoundrel

THINKING IT THROUGH

1. When Thomas Paine wrote his pamphlet, America was bound as a slave to England. Who seeks to bind us today? Why? What methods do they use?

2. What can you do in your life-time to ensure peace for those who come after you?

3. What kind of people are needed to preserve our country? What can you do now to become one of those people?

ABOUT THE AUTHOR

Thomas Paine (1737-1809), an interesting figure of the Revolutionary period, did much by his writings to help win the war. Franklin on one occasion said, "Where liberty is, there is my home"; whereupon Paine answered, "Where liberty is not, there is my home." He came to America from England in 1774 and fought for America's freedom as a volunteer under Washington. After the Revolution he went to France, where again he fought for liberty in the French Revolution.

FREEDOM

—James Russell Lowell

They are slaves who will not choose
Hatred, scoffing and abuse,
Rather than in silence shrink
From the truth they needs must think.
They are slaves who dare not be
In the right with two or three.

A WELL-SPENT LIFE

James T. Fields

Oh, happiest he, whose *riper* years *retain*
The hopes of youth, *unsullied* by a stain!
His eve of life in calm content shall glide,
Like the still streamlet to the ocean tide;
No gloomy cloud hangs o'er his *tranquil* day;
No *meteor lures* him from his home astray;
For him there glows with glittering beam on high
Love's changeless star that leads him to the sky.
Still, to the past he sometimes turns to trace
The mild expression of a mother's face,
And dreams, perchance, as *oft* in earlier years,
The low, sweet music of her voice he hears.

riper — later
retain — keep
unsullied — unsoiled
tranquil — calm
meteor — passing fancy
lures — tempts
oft — often

HOW TO WIN

– C. C. Cameron

Genius, that power which dazzles mortal eyes,
Is oft but *perseverance* in disguise.
  Continuous effort of itself implies,
    In spite of countless falls, the power to rise,
'*Twixt* failure and success the print's so fine,
Men sometimes know not when they touch the line;
Just when the pearl is waiting one more plunge,
How many a struggler has thrown up the sponge.
  As the tide goes clear out it comes clear in;
  In business 'tis at turns, the wisest win;

And, oh, how true when shades of doubt dismay,
" 'Tis often darkest just before the day."
  A little more *persistence*, courage, *vim*,
  Success will dawn o'er failure's cloudy rim.
Then take this honey for the bitterest cup;
There is no failure, save in giving up.
  No real fall, so long as one still tries,
  For seeming set-backs make the strong man wise.
There's no defeat, in truth, save from within;
Unless you're beaten there, you're bound to win.

perseverance — to keep on in spite of opposition or discouragement
'*Twixt* — between
persistence — to go on resolutely in spite of all obstacles
vim — enthusiasm

THINKING IT THROUGH

1. Perseverance is the key to success. How does Mr. Cameron's poem illustrate this principle?
2. Explain the statement, " 'Tis often darkest just before the day."
3. Write an exciting story in which the main character shows perseverance.

CHARACTER

– Margaret Slattery

What one is, that is the supreme thing. Sincerity, honesty, unselfishness, intelligence, the spirit of cooperation and justice, cheerfulness, courtesy, concentration and all the rest help make one what he is. What one is — that is Character. Strong, fine character stands the test of life with all its dangers and pitfalls — nothing else does.

Everyone has the power of making his character what it ought to be. The power lies in the little words "Yes" and "No." Saying "Yes" to all that life offers which is good and right, and saying "No" to all that can weaken or defile, will form character strong, pure and fine.

THINKING IT THROUGH

1. What is a person's character?
2. Explain how the little words "Yes" and "No" can help you to build strong character.

HOW BAMBI FOUND THE MEADOW

Felix Salten

In early summer the trees stood still under the blue sky, held their limbs outstretched, and received the direct rays of the sun. On the shrubs and bushes in the undergrowth, the flowers unfolded their red, white, and yellow stars. On some the seed pods had begun to appear again. They perched innumerable on the fine tips of the branches, tender and firm and resolute, and seemed like small, clenched fists. Out of the earth came whole troops of flowers, like *motley* stars, so that the soil of the twilit forest floor shone with a silent, *ardent* colorful gladness. Everything smelled of fresh leaves, of blossoms, of *moist clods* and green wood. When morning broke, or when the sun went down, the whole woods *resounded* with a thousand voices, and from morning till night, the bees hummed, the wasps droned, and filled the fragrant stillness with their murmur.

These were the earliest days of Bambi's life. He walked behind his mother on a narrow track that ran through the midst of the bushes. How pleasant it was to walk there! The thick *foliage* stroked his flanks softly and bent *supplely* aside. The track appeared to be barred and obstructed in a dozen places and yet they advanced with the greatest ease. There were tracks like this everywhere, running criss-cross through the whole woods. His mother knew them all, and if Bambi sometimes stopped before a bush as if it were an impenetrable green wall, she always found where the path went through, without hesitation or searching.

Bambi questioned her. He loved to ask

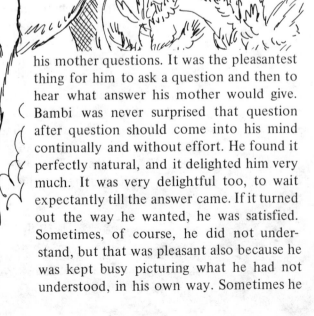

his mother questions. It was the pleasantest thing for him to ask a question and then to hear what answer his mother would give. Bambi was never surprised that question after question should come into his mind continually and without effort. He found it perfectly natural, and it delighted him very much. It was very delightful too, to wait expectantly till the answer came. If it turned out the way he wanted, he was satisfied. Sometimes, of course, he did not understand, but that was pleasant also because he was kept busy picturing what he had not understood, in his own way. Sometimes he felt very sure that his mother was not giving him a complete answer, was intentionally not telling him all she knew. And, at first, that was very pleasant, too. For then there would remain in him such a lively curiosity, such suspicion, mysteriously and joyously flashing through him, such *anticipation*, that he would become anxious and happy at the same time, and grow silent.

Once he asked, "Whom does this trail belong to, Mother?"

His mother answered, "To us."

Bambi asked again, "To you and me?"

"Yes."

"Only to us two?"

"No," said his mother, "to us deer."

"What are deer?" Bambi asked, and laughed.

His mother looked at him from head to foot and laughed too.

"You are a deer and I am a deer. We're both deer," she said. "Do you understand?"

Bambi sprang into the air for joy. "Yes, I understand," he said. "I'm a little deer and you're a big deer, aren't you?"

His mother nodded and said, "Now you see."

But Bambi grew serious again. "Are there other deer besides you and me?" he asked.

"Certainly," his mother said. "Many of them."

"Where are they?" cried Bambi.

"Here, everywhere."

"But I don't see them."

"You will soon," she said.

"When?" Bambi stood still, wild with curiosity.

"Soon." The mother walked on quietly. Bambi followed her. He kept silent for he was wondering what "soon" might mean. He came to the conclusion that "soon" was certainly not "now." But he wasn't sure at what time "soon" stopped being "soon" and began to be a "long while." Suddenly he asked, "Who made this trail?"

"We," his mother answered.

Bambi was *astonished*. "We? You and I?"

The mother said, "We, we...we deer."

Bambi asked, "Which deer?"

"All of us," his mother said sharply.

They walked on. Bambi was in high spirits and felt like leaping off the path, but he stayed close to his mother. Something rustled in front of them, close to the ground. The fern *fronds* and wood lettuce *concealed* something that advanced in violent motion. A threadlike, little cry shrilled out *piteously*; then all was still. Only the leaves and the blades of grass shivered back into place. A *ferret* had caught a mouse. He came slinking by, slid sideways, and prepared to enjoy his meal.

"What was that?" asked Bambi excitedly.

"Nothing," his mother soothed him.

"But," Bambi trembled, "but I saw it."

"Yes, yes," said his mother. "Don't be frightened. The ferret has killed a mouse." But Bambi was dreadfully frightened. A vast, unknown horror clutched at his heart. It was long before he could speak again. Then he asked, "Why did he kill the mouse?"

"Because," his mother hesitated. "Let us walk faster," she said as though something had just occurred to her and as though she had forgotten the question. She began to hurry. Bambi sprang after her.

A long pause ensued. They walked on quietly again. Finally Bambi asked *anx-*

iously, "Shall we kill a mouse, too, sometime?"

"No," replied his mother.

"Never?" asked Bambi.

"Never," came the answer.

"Why not?" asked Bambi, relieved.

"Because we never kill anything," said his mother simply.

Bambi grew happy again.

Loud cries were coming from a young ash tree which stood near their path. The mother went along without noticing them, but Bambi stopped inquisitively. Overhead two jays were quarreling about a nest they had *plundered*.

"Get away, you murderer!" cried one.

"Keep cool, you fool," the other answered. "I'm not afraid of you."

"Look for your own nests," the first one shouted, "or I'll break your head for you." He was beside himself with rage. "What *vulgarity*!" he chattered, "what vulgarity!"

The other jay had spied Bambi and fluttered down a few branches to shout at him. "What are you *gawking* at, you freak?" he screamed.

Bambi sprang away terrified. He reached his mother and walked behind her again, frightened and obedient, thinking she had not noticed his absence.

After a pause he asked, "Mother, what is vulgarity?"

"I don't know," said his mother.

Bambi thought a while; then he began again. "Why were they both so angry with each other, Mother?" he asked.

"They were fighting over food," his mother answered.

"Will we fight over food, too, sometime?" Bambi asked.

"No," said his mother.

Bambi asked, "Why not?"

"Because there is enough for all of us," his mother replied.

Bambi wanted to know something else. "Mother," he began.

"What is it?"

"Will we be angry with each other sometime?" he asked.

"No, child," said his mother, "we don't do such things."

They walked along again. Presently it grew light ahead of them. It grew very bright. The trail ended with the tangle of vines and bushes. A few steps more and they would be in the bright open space that spread out before them. Bambi wanted to bound forward, but his mother had stopped.

"What is it?" he asked impatiently, already delighted.

"It's the meadow," his mother answered.

"What is a meadow?" asked Bambi insistently.

His mother cut him short. "You'll soon find out for yourself," she said. She had become very serious and watchful. She stood motionless, holding her head high and listening *intently*. She sucked in deep breathfuls of air and looked very *severe*.

"It's all right," she said at last, "we can go out."

Bambi leaped forward, but his mother barred the way.

"Wait till I call you," she said. Bambi obeyed at once and stood still. "That's right," said his mother, to encourage him,

"and now listen to what I am saying to you." Bambi heard how seriously his mother spoke and felt terribly excited.

"Walking on the meadow is not so simple," his mother went on. "It's a difficult and dangerous business. Don't ask me why. You'll find that out later on. Now do exactly as I tell you to. Will you?"

"Yes," Bambi promised.

"Good," his mother said, "I'm going out alone first. Stay here and wait. And don't take your eyes off me for a minute. If you see me run back here, then turn around and run as fast as you can. I'll catch up with you soon." She grew silent and seemed to be thinking. Then she went on earnestly. "Run anyway as fast as your legs will carry you. Run even if something should happen . . . even if you should see me fall to the ground. . . Don't think of me, do you understand? No matter what you see or hear, start running right away and just as fast as you possibly can. Do you promise me to do that?"

"Yes," said Bambi softly. His mother spoke so seriously.

She went on speaking. "Out there if I should call you," she said, "there must be no looking around and no questions, but you must get behind me instantly. Understand that. Run without pausing or stopping to think. If I begin to run, that means for you to run too, and no stopping until we are back here again. You won't forget, will you?"

"No," said Bambi in a troubled voice.

"Now I'm going ahead," said his mother, and seemed to become calmer.

She walked out. Bambi, who never took his eyes off her, saw how she moved forward with slow, cautious steps. He stood there full of expectancy, full of fear and curiosity. He saw how his mother listened in all directions, saw her shrink together, and shrank himself, ready to leap back into the thickets. Then his mother grew calm again. She stretched herself. Then she looked around satisfied and called, "Come!"

Bambi bounded out. Joy seized him with such tremendous force that he forgot his worries in a flash. Through the thicket he could see only the green tree-tops overhead. Once in a while he caught a glimpse of the blue sky.

Now he saw the whole heaven stretching far and wide and he rejoiced without knowing why. In the forest he had seen only a stray sunbeam now and then, or the tender, *dappled* light that played through the branches. Suddenly he was standing in the blinding hot sunlight whose boundless power was beaming upon him. He stood in the splendid warmth that made him shut his eyes but which opened his heart.

Bambi was as though bewitched. He was completely beside himself with pleasure. He was simply wild. He leaped into the air three, four, five times. He had to do it. He felt a terrible desire to leap and jump. He stretched his young limbs joyfully. His breath came deeply and easily. He drank in the air. The sweet smell of the meadow made him so wildly happy that he had to leap into the air.

Bambi was a child. If he had been a human child he would have shouted. But he was a young deer, and deer cannot shout, at least not the way human children do. So he rejoiced with his legs and with his whole body as he flung himself into the air. His mother stood by and was glad. She was happy that Bambi was wild. She watched how he *bounded* into the air and fell awkwardly, in one spot. She saw how he stared around him, dazed and bewildered, only to leap up over and over again. She understood that Bambi knew only the narrow deer tracks in the forest and how his brief life was used to the limits of the thicket. He did not move from one place because he did not understand how to run freely around the open meadow.

So she stretched out her forefeet and bent laughingly towards Bambi for a moment. Then she was off with one bound, racing around in a circle so that the tall grass stems swished.

Bambi was frightened and stood motionless. Was that a sign for him to run back to the thicket? His mother had said to him, "Don't worry about me no matter what you see or hear. Just run as fast as you can." He was going to turn and run as she had commanded him to, but his mother came galloping up suddenly. She came up with a wonderful swishing sound and stopped two steps from him. She bent towards him, laughing as she had at first and cried, "Catch me." And in a flash she was gone.

Bambi was puzzled. What did she mean? Then she came back again running so fast that it made him *giddy*. She pushed his flank with her nose and said quickly, "Try to catch me," and fled away.

Bambi started after her. He took a few steps. Then his steps became short bounds. He felt as if he were flying without any effort on his part. There was a space under his hoofs, space under his bounding feet, space and still more space. Bambi was beside himself with joy.

The swishing grass sounded wonderful to his ears. It was marvelously soft and as fine as silk where it brushed against him. He ran round in a circle. He turned and flew off in a new circle, turned around again and kept running. His mother was standing still, getting her breath again. She kept following Bambi with her eyes. He was wild.

Suddenly the race was over. He stopped and came up to his mother, lifting his hoofs elegantly. He looked joyfully at her. Then they strolled *contentedly* side by side.

Since he had been in the open, Bambi had felt the sky and the sun and the green meadow with his whole body. He took one blinding, giddy glance at the sun, and he felt its rays as they lay warmly on his back.

Presently he began to enjoy the meadow with his eyes also. Its wonders amazed him at every step he took. You could not see the tiniest speck of earth the way you could in the forest. Blade after blade of grass covered every inch of ground. It tossed and waved *luxuriantly*. It bent softly aside under every footstep, only to rise up unharmed again. The broad green meadow was starred with white daisies, with the thick, round red and purple clover blossoms and bright golden dandelion heads.

"Look, look, Mother!" Bambi exclaimed. "There's a flower flying."

"That's not a flower," said his mother, "that's a butterfly."

Bambi stared at the butterfly, entranced. It had darted lightly from a blade of grass and was fluttering about in its giddy way. Then Bambi saw that there were many butterflies flying in the air above the meadow. They seemed to be in a hurry and yet moved slowly, fluttering up and down in a sort of game that delighted him. They really did look like gay flying flowers that would not stay on their stems but had unfastened themselves in order to dance a little. They looked, too, like flowers that come to rest at sundown but have no fixed places and have to hunt for them, dropping down and vanishing as if they really had settled somewhere, yet always flying up again, a little way at first, then higher and higher, and always searching farther and farther because all the good places have already been taken.

Bambi gazed at them all. He would have loved to see one close by. He wanted to see one face to face but he was not able to. They sailed in and out continually. The air was aflutter with them.

When he looked down at the ground again, he was delighted with the thousands of living things he saw stirring under his hoofs. They ran and jumped in all directions. He would see a wild swarm of them, and the next moment they had disappeared in the grass again.

"Who are they, Mother?" he asked.

"Look," cried Bambi, "see that piece of grass jumping. Look how high it can jump!"

"That's not grass," his mother explained,

"that's a nice grasshopper."

"Why does he jump that way?" asked Bambi.

"Because we're walking here," his mother answered; "he's afraid we'll step on him."

"O," said Bambi, turning to the grasshopper who was sitting on a daisy; "O," he said again politely, "you don't have to be afraid; we won't hurt you."

"I'm not afraid," the grasshopper replied in a quavering voice; "I was only frightened for a moment when I was talking to my wife."

"Excuse us for disturbing you," said Bambi shyly.

"Not at all," the grasshopper quavered. "Since it's you, it's perfectly all right. But you never know who's coming and you have to be careful."

"This is the first time in my life that I've ever been on the meadow," Bambi explained; "my mother brought me . . ."

The grasshopper was sitting with his head lowered as though he were going to butt. He put on a serious face and murmured, "That doesn't interest me at all, I haven't time to stand here gossiping with you. I have to be looking for my wife. Hopp!" And he gave a jump.

"Hopp!" said Bambi in surprise at the high jump with which the grasshopper vanished.

Bambi ran to his mother. "Mother, I spoke to him," he cried.

"To whom?" his mother asked.

"To the grasshopper," Bambi said, "I spoke to him. He was very nice to me. And I like him so much. He's so wonderful and green and you can see through his sides. They look like leaves, but you can't see through a leaf."

"Those are his wings," said his mother.

"O," Bambi went on, "and his face is so serious and wise. But he was very nice to me anyhow. And how he can jump! 'Hopp!' he said, and he jumped so high I couldn't see anymore."

They walked on. The conversation with the grasshopper had excited Bambi and tired him a little, for it was the first time he had ever spoken to a stranger. He felt hungry and pressed close to his mother to be nursed.

Then he stood quietly and gazed dreamily into space for a little while with a sort of joyous *ecstasy* that came over him every time he was nursed by his mother. He noticed a bright flower moving in the tangled grasses. Bambi looked more closely at it. No, it wasn't a flower, but a butterfly. Bambi crept closer.

The butterfly hung heavily to a grass stem and fanned its wings slowly.

"Please sit still," said Bambi.

"Why should I sit still? I'm a butterfly," the insect answered in *astonishment*.

"O, please sit still, just for a minute," Bambi pleaded. "I've wanted so much to see you close. Please."

"Well," said the butterfly, "for your sake I will, but not for long."

Bambi stood in front of him. "How beautiful you are!" he cried fascinated; "how wonderfully beautiful you are, like a flower!"

"What?" cried the butterfly, fanning his wings, "did you say like a flower? In my circle it's generally supposed that we're handsomer than flowers."

Bambi was embarrassed. "O, yes," he stammered, "much handsomer, excuse me, I only meant . . ."

"Whatever you meant is all one to me," the butterfly replied. He arched his thin body *affectedly* and played with his delicate feelers.

Bambi looked at him enchanted. "How elegant you are!" he said, "How elegant and fine! And how splendid and white your wings are!"

The butterfly spread his wings wide apart, then raised them till they folded together like an upright sail.

"O," cried Bambi, "I know that you are handsomer than the flowers. Besides, you can fly and the flowers can't because they grow on stems, that's why."

The butterfly spread his wings. "It's enough," he said, "that I can fly." He soared so lightly that Bambi could hardly see him or follow his flight. His wings moved gently and gracefully. Then he fluttered into the sunny air.

"I only sat still that long on your account," he said, balancing in the air in front of Bambi. "Now I'm going."

That was how Bambi found the meadow.

affectedly — proudly
anticipation — expectation
anxiously — fearfully
arched — curved
ardent — shining
astonished — surprised
astonishment — surprise
bounded — leaped; jumped
concealed — hid
dappled — spotted
ecstasy — delight
entranced — in wonder
ferret — a European polecat
foliage — leaves

fronds — the leaves of ferns
gawking — staring
giddy — dizzy
inquisitively — questioningly
intently — carefully
moist clods — damp earth
motley — different colored
piteously — pitifully
plundered — robbed
severe — serious
strolled — walked
supplely — bending with ease or grace
vulgarity — coarse language

A LESSON FROM THE SPIDER

Author Unknown

The famous Robert Bruce of Scotland, having been defeated in battle, was *obliged* to hide himself sometimes in the woods, and sometimes in the huts of poor peasants, for his enemies were in pursuit of him and determined to kill him if they could find him.

One morning, after a sleepless night of *anxiety*, he was lying on a heap of straw in a deserted hut, reflecting upon his misfortunes and nearly discouraged. From where he lay he could see a spider trying to swing itself by its thread from one beam of roof to another. It failed, and the thread swung back to its former position.

Bruce's attention was now fully aroused, and his feeling enlisted for the success of the little insect. Again and again the little creature failed, but as often renewed the attempt with *unabated* energy, and, after six unsuccessful efforts, succeeded in the seventh in reaching the desired position.

The lesson of perseverance taught by the spider *roused* the *desponding* hero to new *exertion*. He went forth from his hiding place, assembled his friends, defeated his enemies in a great and decisive battle, and was soon afterward crowned king of Scotland.

THINKING IT THROUGH

1. What lesson did Robert Bruce learn from the spider?
2. How did this lesson help him? How can it help you to meet discouragement?

obliged — forced
anxiety — worry
unabated — full strength or force
roused — stirred
desponding — extremely discouraged
exertion — effort

WHO LOVES HIS COUNTRY

— Nancy Byrd Turner

Who loves his country will not rest
Content with vow and pledge alone,
But flies her banner in his breast
And counts her destiny his own —
Not only when the bugle plays
Stands forth to give his life for her,
But on the field of common days
Is strong to live his life for her.
He is not satisfied to claim
As heritage her power and fame,
But, striving, earns the right to wear
The shining honor of her name.

LAFAYETTE

Smith Burnham

A daring young French nobleman, Marquis de Lafayette, leaves his country to help America win her freedom.

In a great stone building among the tree-covered hills in the south of France there lived a little boy who at birth received fourteen names and titles. He belonged to the noble French family of the Lafayettes, who had been knights for at least seven hundred years. The boy never saw his father, for shortly before the child was born, his brave, young soldier father was killed in a battle with the English. The home in which this fatherless boy lived was a castle, but it looked like a great prison or a modern storage warehouse with a huge, round tower at each end. Across its few small windows were iron bars.

Out of all the Lafayette boy's names, the family called him Gilbert. When he was eleven years old Gilbert was sent to a school in Paris where sons from French gentlemen's families were taught the things it was thought proper for young nobles to know. First of all, they studied heraldry, which explained the coat-of-arms of their royal and noble relations and was really a sort of family history of France. The boys also learned to ride and to fence and to talk politely - - even wittily, if they happened to be bright enough. Besides their own French language they learned Latin so that they could write and even speak it. Then the youths who had a taste for history were instructed in that study, not the history of the whole French people, but the records of the royal and great families, and the battles and schemes of the kings and princes.

In this boys' college the rooms were very small, dark, and narrow, like prison cells, and the pupils were locked in at night. Gilbert was never allowed a holiday. If his mother came to see him she was permitted to talk with him in the presence of a tutor, almost as if he were a prisoner. The masters feared that a good, motherly chat with her son would distract the boy's mind from his studies.

Madame de Lafayette wished to do all she could to help her son in his future life. So she moved to Paris and was presented at court; that is, she was introduced to the king and queen and the highest nobles of France. When Gilbert was thirteen his mother died, leaving her son almost alone in the world. He had a rich uncle who might have been his guardian, but he also died, leaving young Lafayette another fortune and making him a very wealthy marquis.

Boys and girls in French noble families were often betrothed in infancy and brought up expecting to marry each other when old enough. Marriage seemed to be rather a question of the family fortunes than of the young people's real love for each other. When young Marquis de Lafayette was left without parents to plan a proper marriage for him, a rich duke who was a great favorite with King Louis decided to arrange for the orphan boy to marry his own daughter Adrienne. In order to bring this about, Adrienne's parents invited Gilbert de Lafayette to come and live in their palace, where they all could care for him as a son until it was proper for him to marry their daughter. There was a wonderful wedding when Lafayette was sixteen and Adrienne fourteen years old.

From that time, besides all the wealth of the Lafayettes, the riches of his father-in-law, the duke, gave the young marquis a splendid position at the court of France. If the boy bridegroom only had enjoyed that sort of high life he might have been very happy. But the things which interested the young nobleman were of quite a different sort. While he was at a dinner in honor of a younger brother of George the Third, king of England, he heard that the American people across the sea were so aroused that he began at once to plan to leave his palace home, his lovely young wife, and his baby daughter, in order to help the American people in their struggle. To find out how best to do this, he went to see Dr. Franklin and Silas Deane, the agents for the United States in France. Knowing how much the American people needed Lafayette's money and influence, these statesmen encouraged him in every way.

The young marquis fitted out a ship and made ready to start, taking with him several Frenchmen of high rank who also expected to be made officers in the American Army.

But Lafayette's father-in-law did not relish the youth's idea of fighting for the common people against kings and nobles, so he persuaded the king to order the marquis not to leave the country. In spite of King Louis's command, Lafayette walked on board his own ship, under the detectives' noses, disguised as the bodyservant of a stranger from another country who also was going to fight for American liberty.

The Marquis de Lafayette reached the American army, near Philadelphia, after many dangers and hardships. General Washington could not help smiling at the earnestness of Major-General Lafayette, aged nineteen, who could command only as much of the English language as he had learned while crossing the Atlantic. Though the Marquis, as everyone learned to call him, volunteered to serve anywhere without pay, Washington offered him a place on his staff. Once when the commander-in-chief asked Lafayette how to improve the discipline of the American troops, the noble youth replied, "I am here, General, to learn, not to teach."

General Lafayette received his first wound in the Battle of Brandywine, where he fought hard to keep the British back from Philadelphia. While riding his horse at the head of his men, he was shot in the leg. He recovered from this wound in time to come to Valley Forge and suffer with Washington the hardships of the long, bitter winter there.

While at Valley Forge the young general was sent to keep the British from coming out from Philadelphia and attacking the American camp. Lafayette took his station at Barren Hill near the Schuylkill River. When the British commander had word of this, he sent out three companies to surround the boy general from three directions, and make him their prisoner. So sure were they of making this capture that they planned a dinner in honor of their noble French prisoner, and invited their friends of Philadelphia to be present and meet the Marquis de Lafayette.

But the boy general was too shrewd for them all. Quick as a flash he saw a way out of the trap they had set for him. Ordering the heads of his columns to stand in the edge of a grove where they could be seen as if in battle array, he ordered a retreat by a secret path. When the three British lines marched up the hill, even the Americans in the edge of the woods had disappeared, and the companies only met one another and looked sheepish as they marched down

again. Their game had gotten away, and they had to eat that dinner without their prisoner guest.

Howe and his men soon heard that the French were sending ships and men to help their American friends, so they went away from Philadelphia as quickly as possible. On the way to New York, Washington met them and gave battle at Monmouth, New Jersey. He appointed General Lafayette second in command; but General Charles Lee was offended because "that French boy" was placed above him. To relieve his chief, Lafayette gave up the command. This was the battle in which Lee disobeyed Washington's command and prevented the American army from winning a real victory. It was Lafayette who saw that something was going wrong and helped to save the day for the Americans.

Hearing of his wife's illness and his little daughter's death, Lafayette asked leave of absence to go home to France. He returned to America as soon as he could, after persuading the French government to send more money, more men, and more ships to help bring the long war with England to an end. Soon after his return, the Marquis was sent with his regiment to meet Cornwallis and defend Virginia.

Cornwallis laughed when he saw that "the Boy" had been sent against him. But

"the Boy" was more than a match for the British commander in the south. He kept retreating and advancing up and down the James River. One day Cornwallis would think he was trapping Lafayette, but the next day he found himself only moving farther from his base of supplies. "The Boy" did this just to gain time, for he had learned that the expected fleet was in American waters with a French army on board, and that Washington was on his way down from near New York to meet the French ships and men and surround Cornwallis. It was now the British general's turn to retreat. He retired to Yorktown, where he was surrounded by the Americans and French and was soon forced to surrender.

As soon as the fighting was ended, General Washington gave a dinner to the French officers and their English prisoner, Lord Cornwallis. The defeated general was so well treated by Washington and his men that the two commanders became good friends.

When the Americans had gained their independence, General Lafayette returned to France, where he was received as a hero, even by the king whose command he had disobeyed by running away to help America. The people were so fond of the brave young marquis, that King Louis appointed him a marshal of France, even though he was only twenty-four.

The French Revolution soon broke out, but it was very different from the American Revolution, because the people of France had the wrong idea of liberty. They killed the king, the queen, and many of the nobles in a savage and cruel way. They even imprisoned and put to death some of their early leaders, who loved liberty, but who were not willing to do such savage deeds to obtain it.

Lafayette was one of the lovers of liberty who suffered much from the French people during the Revolution, because he did not believe in going to extremes.

Washington and Lafayette did not forget each other. They wrote devoted letters to each other as if they were father and son. The French nobleman named his son for Washington who, during the troublous years in France, received and cared for the boy as if he were a grandson.

Nearly fifty years after Lafayette's first coming to America, he made his fourth voyage to our country, bringing with him his son, George Washington de Lafayette. He came, at the invitation of President Monroe and Congress, as the guest of the United States. Because of the enthusiasm with which he was welcomed all over the country, his visit was remembered as one of the brightest times in the history of the United States.

One hundred and forty years after the Marquis de Lafayette's first coming to help America, four millions of American young men were enrolled to rescue republican France from her brutal enemy. A million soldiers had crossed the ocean, and another million were on their way when a company of Americans visited the last resting place of Lafayette. As they laid a wreath upon the tomb of the "Friend of America," General Pershing, the commander of the American forces, exclaimed, "Lafayette, we are here!"

THINKING IT THROUGH

1. Describe Lafayette.
2. How did he escape to sea under the watchful eye of detectives who were sent to stop him? What does this reveal about him?
3. Once when General Washington asked Lafayette's advice, the young man replied, "I am here, General, to learn, not to teach." What does this tell about his character?
4. How did he help America?

CAP
by Georgene Faulkner

Cap did not have a long pedigree; he was just a plain dog. But one look into his honest brown eyes would tell you that Cap was to be trusted. He had character; he could always be depended upon.

From the time that he was a small puppy he had tried to help everyone upon the farm. He guarded the baby as though he were responsible for the child. As the baby toddled about, Cap walked proudly to his side as much as to say, "I will watch him and see that no one harms him." Sometimes, as they lay side by side in the sunny dooryard, the baby would bury both fat fists in Cap's soft coat and try to pull out handfuls of fur, but Cap never growled.

Once the baby fell face downward into the duck pond and would have drowned; but faithful Cap pulled him out of the water. Then, seizing baby's muddy hat in his mouth, he plunged away to the farm house, barking and calling for help. "Yere-ere-ere-err-yere-ere, come here, ere-ere," barked Cap. The frightened family followed at his heels and soon brought the half-drowned child into the house.

"That puppy is truly a captain," said his master. "He knows just what to do." So, from that day, the dog was named Captain and called "Cap."

The whole family loved the bright little dog, but his special friend was Pierre. Pierre, who was twelve years old on the day that Cap was born, felt that Cap was his birthday present. Pierre trained Cap to come at his call and to go out with him to watch and guard the sheep. Every day the boy and his dog wandered across the hills together. Then, when the sheep were ready to come home, Cap barked at their heels and not one of them dared to disobey his sharp command. "Yere-yere, come here-here!" He was like a captain calling his orders to his soldiers, "Fall in! Forward — March!" The sheep would scurry before him down the dusty road.

One day, when they were far up on the hillside, a lamb fell over the rocky side of the ravine and dropped on the ledge below. "Ma-ma-ma," bleated the lamb, as it cried for its mother.

The mother sheep answering, "Baa-baa, baa-aaa-aa," rushed to the side of the hill. The poor mother sheep, however, not knowing how to reach her frightened baby, called loudly for help.

The day was very warm and Pierre, lying down under a tree, had fallen asleep, while the faithful Cap, stretched out at his side, was resting as he watched the sheep

grazing peacefully on the hillside. Suddenly Cap sat up, and his ears pricked forward as he heard the call of distress. He ran quickly over the rocks and when he saw the lamb down below he gave a loud sharp bark, as much as to say, "Hold on, we will help you."

He knew that he could not reach the lamb, but he knew that his young master could do so. He ran back under the tree and tugged at Pierre's coat until the sleepy shepherd boy was wide awake.

From Cap's actions, the boy knew that a lamb was in trouble. Seizing his shepherd's staff, he climbed up over the rocks, following the excited dog. Cap led him on with sharp barks until they reached the ledge from which the lamb had fallen.

When Pierre looked down, the ledge was so steep that to think of climbing down made him almost dizzy. What could he do? He must not leave the lamb to die.

Cap looked at his master with eager eyes. Pierre would think of some way, he knew, and he, Cap, would help him. Suddenly, remembering a long, strong rope which the boy had brought with him, Cap rushed back. With one end of the rope in his mouth and the rest trailing along behind him, he came back to his young master.

"Good dog, Cap!" said Pierre. "The rope — why, of course, that is the only way."

Then, tying one end of the rope to a tree on the top of the hill and the other end around his own body, he lowered himself over the side of the rocks. He took the staff in his hand because he saw that he could not reach the lamb without it. At last he reached the end of the rope and then, leaning far over, he put the staff under the lamb and lifted it up. But, as he looked over the rocky ravine, he wondered how he could climb back with the lamb in his arms. A misstep would mean sure death for them both. Cap was barking wildly overhead and the mother sheep was bleating mournfully. The boy shut his teeth, and, looking up toward the sky, he prayed, "Oh, God, help me!"

Instantly, his prayer was answered, for he knew just what to do. Untying the rope from his body, he tied it around the lamb and, leaning against a scrubby pine tree for support, he called, "Hey, Cap! Hey, Cap!" The dog looked down, and realizing at once that he must work with his teeth, he pulled up the lamb. Then he tugged at the rope until he freed the lamb, and the frightened creature curled up safely by his mother.

With the free end of the rope in his mouth, Cap went to the ledge and dropped it over toward the boy. The rope caught in the branches of the pine tree; but Pierre pulled it down with his staff and tied it securely around his waist. As he began his *perilous* climb up the rocks, the big dog at the top barked his encouragement.

At last the boy reached the top of the rocks. His clothing was torn and his legs and arms were bruised and bleeding, but he was safe and he knew that the lamb was safe also. Weak and dizzy with a sprained ankle, he fell upon the ground, exhausted. Cap licked the face and hands of his young master and then, when he did not get up and walk, became excited again. He said as plainly as a dog can talk, "Lie here and rest, while I go for help."

Cap took his young master's cap in his teeth and ran down into the valley where the farmer and his older son were reaping. The farmer at once knew that something serious had happened; they fol-

perilous — dangerous

lowed Cap up the hillside where they found Pierre. The rope, fastened to him, and tied about the tree, together with his bruised body, told them the story.

"My boy," said the father. "You should not have risked your life for a lamb."

"Why, I did not do it alone, father," said the boy. "Cap knew just what to do and he helped me."

"Good dog, Cap!" said the farmer. He patted the dog on the head, and Cap licked his hand to show that he knew he was appreciated.

Pierre suffered so much from the sprained ankle and from his bruises that for a time he could not watch the flock. But Cap had proved that he could be trusted to look after the sheep. For a while the shepherd dog went out alone to the hillside. When the boy was better, they went out together to take care of the flock. Many happy days they spent wandering over the hills, for the boy and his dog were inseparable friends.

"Cap is my best friend," said Pierre. "He always understands everything I say

to him. I know that he loves me and I love him dearly."

The years went on and war came to the peaceful valley. Pierre was now a young man, eighteen years old, and glad that he was to march away and serve his country.

Across the green pastures, ugly trenches were dug and barbed wire coils were tangled everywhere. No sheep were grazing upon the hillside now. They had all been sold and killed for food, while the dog, Captain, had been given to the ambulance corps.

"My son has gone to the front," said the father proudly, "and I shall go too, when I am needed. This shepherd dog, Captain, is his dog. I know that my boy will be glad to have his dog in service, also. He is a good dog, Cap."

Cap was soon trained by the Red Cross Society to search out the wounded upon the battlefield and to bring them help. Cap was very proud of his harness, with its relief supplies and tiny canteens, and of his red cross and badge of service. From the first day, he showed his ability to look after the wounded soldiers.

"That dog is the kindest and most faithful animal in the whole lot," said the young doctor who trained Cap for the service. "The other day Captain saved thirty lives by his persistent searching on the battlefield. We know when Cap comes back, holding a hat in his mouth, that there is some one out there whom we can help, and he leads us to the place at once. Why, that dog almost talks, he is so intelligent."

One day during frightful firing across the trenches, the dogs and men suffered from the deadly fumes of poisonous gas. The doctor put a mask over Cap's face to protect him from the gases. Cap seemed to know that the mask was for his own good and, although he had never worn a muzzle in his life, he did not growl but went right on with his work.

When the firing ceased and the fumes had passed away, the mask was removed from Cap. He ran out into the valley of death, into the "no man's land" of the dead and wounded, and sniffed about to find some one to help. At last he was rewarded by finding a young soldier who was alive. As he sniffed the wounded soldier, his tail wagged in joy and he suddenly broke the law of the Red Cross dogs and barked in his excitement – he had found his own master!

Pierre had fallen upon his face. But Cap soon pushed him over upon his back. The sharp barking of the dog aroused the soldier, who, gazing upward, looked into the eyes of his faithful friend. "Cap – oh, Cap," gasped Pierre. "Good dog, did you come for me? Too late now, Cap," and Pierre groaned as he closed his eyes.

Cap began to lick Pierre's face with his tongue, as much as to say, "You must keep awake and I will help you." Pierre opened his eyes and looked again at Cap. Then, seeing the flask carried in the harness of the dog, he seized it eagerly and, taking a drink, he said, "You are right, Cap, I will brace up until you bring some one to help me.'

The dog took the young soldier's cap between his teeth and ran back to the hospital tent. As he put the hat down, he barked again, sharply, as much as to say, "Do come quickly!"

"Now, Cap, none of that," said the doctor. "We will go to your soldier, but you must not command us."

Soon the ambulance men followed the excited dog to the young soldier, who had fainted again. Cap began to lick Pierre's hands and to kiss his face.

"Here, Cap, down," said the young doctor. "You must not be rough with your caresses."

But the wounded soldier boy opened his eyes, and said, "My dog – good dog – Cap – saved my life, when I went for a lost lamb, once – Now, again – just in time – good dog – Cap."

Cap walked slowly behind the ambulance that carried his master to the hospital, where he stretched out by the door, waiting and watching. All night long he watched and waited; he would not go out in the field again, for his own master might need him.

The doctor, who understood dogs as well as men, would not let them order the dog away. "Look at his big eyes. He is suffering with his young master. No, Cap shall stay here and watch. The other dogs can do the field work." He took off the harness from Cap and let him stay on guard at the door.

Cap watched for several days and nights, and every time the door opened he would look anxiously at the doctor. "All right, Cap, your master will pull through," said the doctor at last.

Sure enough, that day Pierre opened his eyes to the world again. His delirium had passed. He asked for Cap and the dog was brought in. With his paws resting on his master's cot, Cap looked lovingly into his face.

"You saved my life, Cap, and when I am well and strong I will go back into the trenches. We must both fight for France, you and I, and now, old Cap, you must go back to the field and look after the wounded. I shall be all right again and will do my part, but Cap, you must go back now. Good-by, good dog, Cap!"

Cap gave his head a shake and then, looking earnestly at his young master, he licked Pierre's face and hands. After this good-by caress, he trotted out and stood at attention before the doctor.

The doctor understood and buckled on Cap's Red Cross uniform and fitted him out for field work again. Then he bent over the dog and, patting him upon his head, he said the very words of the young master: "Good-by, Cap; good dog, Cap!"

THINKING IT THROUGH

1. Name several incidents which prove that Cap was an unusual dog.
2. How did Cap save Pierre's life the first time? the second time?
3. How did the doctor show that he understood Cap's anxiety for Pierre?

OUR COUNTRY

— Author Unknown

Our country! 'tis a glorious land!
   With broad arms stretched from shore to shore,
The proud Pacific chafes her strand,
   She hears the dark Atlantic roar;
And, nurtured on her ample breast,
   How many a godly *prospect* lies
In Nature's wildest grandeur dressed,
   Enameled with her loveliest dyes.

Rich prairies, decked with flowers of gold
   Like sunlit oceans roll afar;
Broad lakes her *azure* heavens behold,
   Reflecting clear each trembling star;
And mighty rivers, mountain born,
   Go sweeping onward, dark and deep,
Through forests where the bounding fawn
   Beneath their sheltering branches leap.

Great God! we thank thee for this home,
   This *bounteous* birth-land of the free;
Where wanderers from afar may come,
   And breathe the air of liberty!
Still may her flowers untrampled spring,
   Her harvests wave, her cities rise;
And yet, till Time shall fold his wing,
   Remain earth's loveliest paradise!

prospect — scene
azure — blue
bounteous — generous; openhanded

You can almost hear a chuckle and see the twinkle in his eye as Uncle Remus narrates the delightful, human-like antics of Brer Rabbit and his forest neighbors to a little boy who comes to visit him.
Brer Rabbit again manages to outsmart his wily old enemy, Brer Fox, in the tale of the two buckets in the well.

OLD MR. RABBIT,
HE'S A GOOD FISHERMAN

Joel Chandler Harris

"Brer Rabbit and Brer Fox were like some children that I know," said Uncle Remus, regarding the little boy, who had come to hear another story, with an *affectation* of great *solemnity*. "Both of 'em were always after one another, a prankin' and a pestrin' around. But Brer Rabbit did have some peace because Brer Fox had gotten *skittish* about puttin' the clamps on Brer Rabbit.

"One day, when Brer Rabbit, and Brer Fox, and Brer Coon, and Brer Bear, and a whole lot of 'em were clearing up a new-ground for to plant 'em a *roastin'-ear* patch, the sun *commenced* to get sorta hot, and Brer Rabbit got tired. But he didn't let on, 'cause he was afraid the rest of 'em would call him lazy. He just kept on carryin' off trash and pilin' up brush, 'til by-and-by he hollered out that he had a brier in his hand — and then he slipped off, and hunted for a cool place to rest. He looked around for a spell, and after awhile he came across a well with a bucket hangin' on it.

" 'That looks cool,' says Brer Rabbit." says he, 'an' cool I expect she is. I'll just get right in there and take me a nap.' And with that he jumped in the bucket he did. But he had hardly started to make himself comfortable than the bucket started to go down into the well."

"Wasn't the Rabbit scared, Uncle Remus?" asked the little boy.

"Honey, there has never been a worse scared beast since the world began than this same Brer Rabbit. He was fairly shakin' all over. He knew where he came from, but he didn't know where he was goin'. Pretty soon he felt the bucket hit the water and there she sat and floated. But Brer Rabbit kept mighty still because he didn't know what minute was going to be his last. He just lay there in the bucket and he shook and he shivered.

"Now Brer Fox he always has one eye on Brer Rabbit, and when he saw that scamp sneak off from the new-ground, Brer Fox he sneaked right after him. He knew Brer Rabbit was up to some project or other, and

Brer Fox crept off to watch him. Brer Fox saw Brer Rabbit come to the well and stop, and then he saw him jump into the bucket, and then — lo and behold — he saw him go down right out of sight. Well, sir, Brer Fox was the most *astonished* Fox that you've ever laid eyes on. He sat out there in the bushes and he *studied* and he studied, but didn't make head nor tails of this kind of business.

"Then he says to himself, says he, 'Well, if this don't bang my times,' says he. 'Right down there in that well is where Brer Rabbit keeps his money hid. And if it isn't that, then he's gone and discovered a gold-mine. And if it isn't that, then I'm going to see what it is in there,' says he.

"Brer Fox crept up a little nearer, he did, and he listened, but he didn't hear any fuss. And he kept on creepin' and gettin' nearer and yet he didn't hear anything down in the well. By-and-by he got right up close and peeped down, but he didn't see anything and he didn't hear anything.

"Now all this time Brer Rabbit was mighty near scared out of his skin. He was afraid to move because the bucket might turn right over and spill him out in the water.

"And while he was down there saying his prayers like a train of cars running down a track, old Brer Fox hollered out, 'Heyo,

Brer Rabbit! Who you visitin' down there?' says he.

" 'Who? Me? Oh, I'm just a fishin', Brer Fox,' says Brer Rabbit, says he. 'I just said to myself that I'd sorta surprise you all with a mess of fish for dinner, and so here I am, and there's the fish. I'm a fishing for suckers, Brer Fox,' says Brer Rabbit, says he.

" 'Are there many of them down there, Brer Rabbit?' says Brer Fox, says he.

" 'Lots of 'em, Brer Fox. Scores and scores of them. The water is just naturally alive with 'em. Come down and help me haul 'em in, Brer Fox,' says Brer Rabbit, says he.

" 'How am I goin' to get down, Brer Rabbit?'

" 'Jump in the other bucket hangin' up there, Brer Fox. It'll fetch you down all safe an' sound.'

"Brer Rabbit talked so happy and talked so sweet that Brer Fox jumped right in the bucket, he did. And as he went down, of course his weight pulled Brer Rabbit up. When they passed one another at the half-

way place, Brer Rabbit sang out:

" 'Good-by, Brer Fox, take care of your
    clothes,
For this is the way the world goes;
Some go up and some go down,
You'll get to the bottom all safe an'
    sound.'

"Soon as Brer Rabbit got out, he gal-loped right off and told the folks that Brer Fox was down in there muddyin' up the drinkin' water. And then he galloped back to the well and hollered down to Brer Fox:

" 'Here come a man with a great big gun —
When he hauls you up, you jump an'
    run.' "

"What then, Uncle Remus?" asked the little boy, as the old man paused.

"In just about half an hour, honey, both of 'em were back in the new-ground workin' like they had never heard of a well — except that every now and then Brer Rabbit would burst out in a laugh, and old Brer Fox would get a spell of the dry grins."

affectation — pretense
astonished — surprised
commenced — began
roastin'-ear — corn
skittish — uneasy
solemnity — seriousness
studied — thought

ABOUT THE AUTHOR

Joel Chandler Harris (1848-1908) began his literary career as an apprentice on a weekly Georgia plantation paper. Here he heard and set down the delightful Negro folk tales which he later retold through the jolly old story-teller, Uncle Remus. These zestful, happy tales won nationwide acclaim for this able American writer.

THE GIRL THAT SAVED THE STOCKADE

One evening in autumn, in the year 1776, there came bad news to a little settlement on the banks of the Ohio River, near where the city of Wheeling now stands.

A scout who had been sent into the forest to learn what danger lurked in the neighborhood reported that the Indians were on the warpath.

He had heard their terrible whoops, had seen a smoldering blockhouse which they had burned, and had watched a party of them as, daubed with war paint and bristling with feathers, they moved swiftly in single file along a forest trail.

"To the stockade!" cried Colonel Sheppard, when he heard the evil tidings. But the settlers were already leaving their cabins and walking quickly and silently towards the log fort, which was their only protection.

As the men, women, and children passed through the gate, two captains, Silas and Ebenezer Zane by name, stood by, making sure that none were missing.

It was not long before a war whoop was heard in the forest, and the fight began. The woods seemed full of savages. They outnumbered the men and boys in the fort five to one.

But the women and girls counted for something in the fights of those days. While the men and boys, as sharpshooters, thrust their long rifles through the loopholes, the women and girls were by no means idle. For there were bullets to be cast from the molten lead. There were the guns, overheated from rapid firing, to be cooled, reloaded, and passed to the men at the loopholes.

A day and a night wore slowly away. Without food or sleep, and almost without water, these brave men, women and young people stood their posts.

Again and again the savages made a rush, under cover of smoke, to storm the fort or to set it on fire. Each time they were driven back.

After the last attack, when they had retired into the woods to plan some new mischief, Colonel Sheppard called a council of war.

"The powder has almost given out," he said. "There is not enough for half a dozen rounds."

The settlers looked at one another very soberly. What could even the bravest do without powder?

"There's a keg of powder in my cabin," said Captain Ebenezer Zane, "but it is sixty yards away."

To cross that space before the eyes of those savages meant death.

Yes, but the Indians were sure to come back and make another attack. The settlers must have powder, or give up the fort. If they surrendered, the men would be tortured at the stake, and the women and children taken into captivity or put to death.

"We must have powder," said the colonel to his men; "and there's none nearer than Captain Zane's cabin. Who will volunteer?"

Every man and boy in that band of heroes wished to go.

"No, no, indeed! Not a man shall go; we haven't one to spare. Let me go!" cried Elizabeth Zane, a fair young girl, sister of Captain Zane.

In vain they tried to keep her back.

"No, Betty, you must not run the risk!" cried all the men; "you'll be killed!"

"Besides, Betty, you can't run fast enough; you are only a girl," said a boy.

"But I am going," Elizabeth said. "You have wasted too much time already. Look at those Indians creeping out of the woods."

The men and boys looked ashamed.

"Let me go; I can run as fast as any of you," said the girl. "If I am killed, I shall not be missed as a man would be. Somebody pin up my hair, so it won't be loose for the Indians to catch hold of."

Carefully the big gate was opened just wide enough for Elizabeth to slip out. She gave one loving look at her brothers. Her dark eyes were shining, but in her face there was not a sign of fear as she walked slowly across the open space to her brother's log cabin.

The Indians hiding in the bushes saw the gate open and gazed in wonder to see the girl, bareheaded, and with sleeves rolled up, quietly walk out of the fort as if for a morning stroll.

"Squaw! squaw!" they shouted, but did not fire a shot.

Elizabeth had now reached the cabin and found the keg of powder.

In breathless silence the watchers at the loopholes saw the girl appear in the doorway with the keg of powder clasped in her arms. She stopped a moment and gave a quick glance at the fort, which seemed a long way off.

"Now it is death to my poor sister! Why did we ever let her go?" said Zane, as he saw the young girl making ready to run back.

Pulling her skirts tight around her, and hugging the keg, Elizabeth started for the fort as fast as she could run.

The Indians set up a yell. They knew now what the girl was doing.

Crack! crack! crack! sounded the rifles of the savages.

The bullets whistled past her, but not one hit her. Almost at the gate, the excited girl stumbled and fell.

Was she hit?

No.

She picked herself up and ran for her life.

Ping! ping! sang the bullets; but in another moment the great gate was opened, and Elizabeth fell into the arms of her brother, who stood ready to catch her.

"Three cheers for Betty Zane!" cried the colonel, and they were given with a will.

With Elizabeth unharmed, and plenty of powder, they all took fresh courage.

The worst, however, was over. Before sunrise the next morning, mounted riflemen from other settlements came to the help of the fort. The Indians now gave up hope. After killing the live stock and setting fire to some cabins, they hurried across the Ohio.

Twenty years afterward, Captain Ebenezer Zane founded the town of Zanesville, Ohio, which is now a flourishing city.

As for his brave sister, she kept the beauty of her youth even to old age. She lived to tell the story of the gunpowder to her grandchildren.

"But never," said one young girl who heard the story from her lips, "did she speak of it boastfully or as a wonderful matter."

THINKING IT THROUGH

1. How did the women and girls help in the battle? the boys?
2. Who volunteered to leave the fort to get gun powder?
3. Why did Betty insist on going?
4. Do you think this is a true story? Why?

MERCY

—Shakespeare

The quality of mercy is not strained;
It droppeth as the gentle rain from heaven
Upon the place beneath: it is twice blest;
It blesseth him that gives and him that takes:
'Tis mightiest in the mightiest; it becomes
The throned monarch better than his crown;
His sceptre shows the force of temporal power,
The attribute to awe and majesty,
Wherein doth sit the dread and fear of kings;
But mercy is above this sceptered sway;
It is enthroned in the hearts of kings;
It is an attribute to God himself.

FEAR OF DEATH

—Shakespeare

Cowards die many times before their death;
The valiant never taste of death but once.
Of all the wonders that I yet have heard,
It seems to me most strange that men should fear;
Seeing that death, a necessary end,
Will come when it will come.

BOY WANTED
Frank Crane

A boy who stands straight, sits straight, acts straight, and talks straight.

A boy who listens carefully when spoken to, who asks questions when he does not understand, and does not ask questions about things that are none of his business.

A boy whose finger-nails are not *in mourning*, whose ears are clean, whose shoes are polished, whose clothes are brushed, whose hair is combed, and whose teeth are well cared for.

A boy who moves quickly and makes as little noise about it as possible.

A boy who whistles in the street but not where he ought to keep still.

A boy who looks cheerful, has a ready smile for everybody, and never sulks.

A boy who is polite to every man and respectful to every woman and girl.

A boy who does not smoke and has no desire to learn how.

A boy who never bullies other boys or allows boys to bully him.

A boy who, when he does not know a thing, says: "I do not know"; and when he has made a mistake says: "I'm sorry"; and, when requested to do anything, immediately says: "I'll try."

A boy who looks you right in the eye and tells the truth every time.

A boy who would rather lose his job or be expelled from school than tell a lie or be a cad.

A boy who is more eager to know how to speak good English than to talk slang.

A boy who does not want to be "smart" nor in anywise attract attention.

A boy who is eager to read good, wholesome books.

A boy whom other boys like.

A boy who is perfectly at ease in the company of respectable girls.

A boy who is not a *goody-goody*, a *prig*, or a little *Pharisee*, but just healthy, happy, and full of life.

A boy who is not sorry for himself and not forever thinking and talking about himself.

A boy who is friendly with his mother and more *intimate* with her than with any one else.

A boy who makes you feel good when he is around.

This boy is wanted everywhere. The family wants him, the school wants him, the office wants him, the boys and girls want him, and all creation wants him.

in mourning — black
goody-goody — pretended goodness
prig — an irritating person who does right in an obnoxious way

Pharisee — a hypocrite; one who pretends to be what he is not
intimate — closely acquainted

GIRLS WANTED
Author Unknown

The girls that are wanted are good girls —
　Good from the heart to the lips,
Pure as the lily is white and pure
　From its heart to its sweet leaf-tips.

The girls that are wanted are home girls —
　Girls that are mother's right hand,
That fathers and mothers can trust in,
　And the little ones understand —

Girls that are fair on the hearthstone,
　And pleasant when nobody sees;
Kind and sweet to their own folks,
　Ready and anxious to please.

The girls that are wanted are wise girls,
　That know what to do and say,
That drive with a smile and a loving word
　The gloom of the household away.

THINKING IT THROUGH

1. What kind of girl does this author say is wanted?
2. Explain what is meant by being "pleasant when nobody sees."
3. How can you "drive with a smile and a loving word the gloom of the household away"?

Daniel Boone's fame has survived the test of time
so that even today his courageous adventures send a thrill of pride
to American hearts. As you read this selection, look for the unique personal qualities
that enabled him to conquer a hostile wilderness
and that caused even his enemies to admire him.

DANIEL BOONE
Stewart Edward White

A new difficulty arose in Boonesborough. There was no salt. Because of the constant alarms of the summer just past, no food remained but *venison*, corn bread and turnips. This was a monotonous enough diet, but it was particularly *insipid* without salt. Sickness threatened. By Christmas the situation was desperate. The long journey over the mountains for such a *commodity* was *appalling*; and as it was now midwinter, and as Indians were rarely on the warpath at that time of the year, the settlers agreed to send a party of men to boil out a supply from the springs at Blue Licks. This was no light job. They would need to boil down from five to eight hundred gallons of the water to produce a single bushel of salt. So you can imagine the time it would take to get an adequate supply with only makeshift cooking kettles.

Boone gathered a party of thirty men from the three forts, partly of the borderers, partly of the militia reinforcements. With a few pack horses carrying only the kettles, axes, and bedding, they started out. For food they were to depend entirely on Boone's rifle. The winter was severe, and even at the salt-making around the fire the little party suffered *acutely*. This hindered the work, but after some weeks they sent back three men with laden pack horses. They got through safely, to the great joy of the people.

But about the second week in February the work came to an end with dramatic suddenness. The weather was intensely cold; so cold that when Boone, hunting in a blinding snowstorm, encountered a large party of Indians, he was too benumbed to outrun the first dash of their young men. With his characteristic good sense he offered no resistance whatever when he saw that resistance would be useless; but dropping the butt of his long rifle on the ground, he laughed good-naturedly, as though the joke were on him. Instantly he was surrounded by a large war party, curious, triumphant, overjoyed — for they recognized Boone at once. Indeed, in this party were his captors of eight years before, who laughed heartily at finding him again in their hands. The Indians shook his hand, patted him on the shoulder, called him "brother," for so famous was he on the border that the savages would rather have captured him than George Washington himself. In the meantime, Boone's keen brain, behind his careless *exterior*, had been swiftly noting details. He saw by its paint and equipment that this was a war party. He could see that it was a serious war party by its numbers, and that it was an important war party by its discipline, its leadership, the presence with it of two Frenchmen, and the fact that, contrary to all custom, it had taken the warpath in the dead of winter. There could be no doubt that the expedition had a definite object; and that object could be no other than the capture of Boonesborough. Also there could be no doubt that the Indians knew that so many of the *garrison* were away. Indeed, the fact that they apparently had intended to pass by the salt-makers without trying to gather their tempting scalps proved plainly enough the single-mindedness of their purpose and the danger to Boonesborough.

All these things Boone saw clearly as he leaned on his long rifle and smiled in the faces of his enemies; and in that few moments he made up his mind to a course of action. He knew not only the fort's weakness in numbers, but that one side of its stockade was even then being *reconstructed*. The presence of the women and children at the fort made the *merest* chance of its capture unthinkable.

Boone greeted the chief of the Indians, Blackfish, with *cordiality*. Under the fierce *scrutiny* of the crowding warriors, he showed

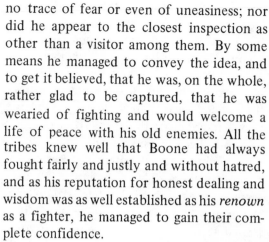

no trace of fear or even of uneasiness; nor did he appear to the closest inspection as other than a visitor among them. By some means he managed to convey the idea, and to get it believed, that he was, on the whole, rather glad to be captured, that he was wearied of fighting and would welcome a life of peace with his old enemies. All the tribes knew well that Boone had always fought fairly and justly and without hatred, and as his reputation for honest dealing and wisdom was as well established as his *renown* as a fighter, he managed to gain their complete confidence.

He then went on to persuade them that he might be able to convince all his people at Boonesborough to move farther north, among friendly Indians, rather than to remain here on the dark and bloody ground, exposed to constant danger and alarm. He proposed that they test him by allowing him to persuade the salt-makers to surrender peaceably. Then he suggested that in the spring, when the weather was warmer, they should all return to Boonesborough properly equipped with horses to carry the women and children. Thus the whole settlement would be content to move north, to live from that time on as the adopted children of the Shawnees. This he made sound entirely reasonable. His *extraordinary* influence over the Indians always had excited much wonder; but it was simply that he possessed all the qualities they particularly admired, and was in addition calm, just, and merciful.

After a long conference he succeeded in influencing Blackfish to turn aside to gather in the salt-makers. In return for a promise of good treatment for them all, Boone guaranteed they would surrender peaceably. When they were within a short distance of the camp, the Indians permitted Boone to advance alone—which in itself shows confidence in his word—to talk with his comrades. The latter agreed to follow his advice *implicitly* — another evidence of confidence, this time on the part of the white man — and so laid down their arms and surrendered.

There was difficulty now. Many of the Shawnee warriors claimed that in this *negotiation* they had not been *consulted*; they had come far on the warpath, and they were *loath* to turn back now without scalps. The Indians called a council, which lasted two hours. Blackfish struggled *vehemently* in debate. Boone was asked again to state his plan, which he did through the interpretation of a Negro named Pompey, who was now a member of the tribe. At last it came to a vote. They had no thought to kill Boone himself, but they debated whether to kill the salt-makers. The war club was passed from one warrior to another. If he struck the ground with it he voted for death; if he passed it silently to his neighbor he voted for *clemency*. Fifty-nine struck the earth; sixty-one passed the war club!

But though the vote was so close, the warriors accepted the decision as final, and thereafter they treated the captives scrupulously well.

They returned at once to the Indian town of Old Chillicothe, and even Boone says it was an uncomfortable journey, for the weather was still very cold. They arrived on the eleventh day. As usual when returning with captives, the war party stopped outside the town to dress and paint, and to strip a pole, on the end of which was hung a "conjuring bag" containing locks of hair from each of the prisoners. Then Blackfish gave three yells, and the band began to sing and to dance around the stripped pole. At once the squaws and boys rushed out to the scene of celebration, while the warriors who had remained at home from the expedition retired in dignity to the council house. The squaws carried in the baggage, leaving the arriving warriors, in their gala paint, free to make a grand entrance, and to dance around the town's war post. This they did for about twenty minutes, after which they entered the council house with their prisoners.

This and more elaborate ceremonies took place always. Blackfish was exceedingly proud of the number and quality of his prisoners.

After the people of Chillicothe had admired the prisoners to their hearts' content, the chief began to desire further praise. He devised a grand tour, which was to end at Detroit, then the British headquarters. His braves took Boone and ten other white men and started out as a sort of traveling circus with exhibits. Everywhere they received good treatment, and at the end of twenty days arrived in Detroit.

They stayed at Detroit for about a month, camping, as was usual with Indians, outside the town. At this time Hamilton was in command, and under him were many officers, and with them white women of rank. In its small way this was a brilliant society. To the Shawnee it was a proud matter to have this *celebrated* prisoner to show off as his property. And the prisoner was indeed celebrated. The English crowded to view him as a curiosity; but soon were overcome by the simplicity and directness and charm of his character. Almost immediately the rough frontiersman was sought and entertained by the most exclusive of these English gentlemen and ladies, people who were usually *profoundly contemptuous* of "uncouth and illiterate backwoodsmen." Soon they gave a more *substantial guarantee* of their interest. Governor Hamilton himself tried to ransom Boone from his Indian captors, and gradually raised his price to one hundred pounds sterling, which was an enormous sum for such a purpose in those days and at the value money bore then. But Blackfish steadily refused. As we have hinted, Boone had succeeded only too well with his captors. He had gained not only their confidence but their affection. Blackfish flatly refused to ransom him at any price. As the British alliance with the Indians was hanging in the balance, Hamilton did not dare press the matter. The other white men were freely left as prisoners of war with the British, a fate infinitely preferable to what would have happened to them if Boone had not made terms for them. But Boone himself they intended to keep. Having failed at their ransom attempt, the English officers made up a sum of money which they offered the scout as a gift for his immediate *necessities*. Boone *declined* this kind offer with gratitude, but with dignity, saying simply that he "looked forward through the *probabilities* of his life, and saw no *prospect* of his being able to repay."

The savages, with Boone, returned over the hard and difficult journey to Old Chillicothe. Then they settled down and adopted Boone into the tribe.

The ceremony of adoption was very formal, and somewhat painful. Blackfish took the scout into his own family, where, as Boone says, "I became a son, and had a great share in the affection of my new parents, brothers, sister, and friends."

First of all, an old Indian squatted down in front of him and began slowly and ceremoniously to pull out all his hair, with the exception of the scalp lock on the crown; "as if he had been plucking a turkey," James Smith describes the process. "He had," Smith adds, "some ashes on a piece of bark, in which he frequently dipped his fingers in order to get a firmer hold." He then divided the scalp lock into three parts, two of which he wrapped about with narrow beaded bands, while the third he braided and ornamented with silver broaches. The men instructed Boone to remove his clothes and put on a breech clout. They painted his face and body in ceremonial colors and patterns, and decorated him with a neck belt of *wampum*, and with silver bracelets and armlets. All this took place within the house. The chief then took him by the hand and led him into the street and uttered the alarm yell rapidly several times. Immediately the whole village came running. Still holding Boone by the hand, Blackfish made a long speech, after which the tribe took their new member to the river and scrubbed him thoroughly from head to foot. This was supposed to wash out the white blood. They gave him a white staff ornamented with deertails, and returned him to the lodge of his captor, Blackfish.

In the case of the usual captive, the family then had a choice of whether he should be killed or adopted; but as this had already been decided, Boone was taken to the great council house. This was a long structure without partitions, with a door at each end, over which was drawn the totem animal of the tribe, and on the doorposts of which were carved the faces of old men, emblems of *gravity* and wisdom. Running the length of the walls were raised benches, or bunks, covered with mats of rushes. Here other members of the tribe had already

brought presents of clothes. Besides the useful hunters' *garments* and blankets there were other things, such as a new ruffled shirt, a pair of leggings decorated with ribbons and beads, a pair of moccasins and garters adorned with beads, porcupine quills, and red hair, and a tinsel lace cloak. Now Boone's face and body were again painted, in new colors and designs, and a bunch of straight red feathers tied to his scalp lock. He was presented with a pipe, a tomahawk, flint and steel, and a tobacco pouch, and made to sit on a bearskin. Next entered into the council house all the warriors of the tribe in ceremonial paint, and wearing all the finery they owned. They seated themselves in a circle along the walls of the council house, and for a time there was a *profound* silence while the smoke curled upward from their pipes. After a time, Blackfish arose and made a speech.

"My son," he said, "you are now flesh of our flesh and bone of our bone. By the ceremony which was performed this day every drop of white blood was washed out of your veins; you were taken into the Shawnee nation and initiated into a warlike tribe; you were adopted into a great family, and now received in the place of a great man."

(Smith's report states that the new member was supposed to fill in the family the place of an Indian who had been killed.)

"You are now one of us by an old, strong law and custom. My son, you have nothing to fear; we are now under the same *obligations* to love, support, and defend you that we are to love and defend one another. Therefore you are to consider yourself one of our people."

Personal introductions then took place, as at a reception. The evening was spent in feasting. Boone was given a bowl and a wooden spoon. The feast was of venison and corn boiled together in brass kettles, maple sugar, bear's fat, and hominy. From that time on, no distinction was made between him and the other members of the tribe. He said, "If they had plenty of clothing, I had plenty; if they were in want, all shared one fate."

Boone was named Sheltowee, or Big Turtle, and taken into the lodge of Blackfish. The chances of escape were practically nothing; so Boone, with his usual wisdom entered so heartily into the life of the tribe and its occupations that he soon gained their entire confidence. In his own words: "I was exceedingly friendly and familiar with them, always appearing as cheerful and satisfied as possible, and they put great confidence in me. The Shawnee king took great notice of me, and treated me with profound respect and entire friendship, often trusting me to hunt at my liberty." In this the Indians took only one precaution; they counted the bullets issued to Boone, and required him to give a very exact accounting when he returned. Boone discovered that a half bullet with a light powder charge was accurate enough, if implanted in just the right spot, to bring down game at close range; so he cut his bullets in two, took special pains in his stalking, and thus managed to *accumulate* a store of ammunition under the Shawnees' very noses.

In the spring the Indians, remembering the occupation of the whites when captured, took Boone to a salt spring on the Scioto and set to boiling out salt. It was hard and *monotonous* work, not at all to the taste of an Indian warrior; but Boone, with his usual generous spirit, worked patiently and efficiently at it. He was only lightly guarded, but he was guarded; and after carefully considering all the chances, he decided against an attempt to escape, and he returned to Chillicothe. He had now been in the Indian town over four months, in all of which time he did not give the faintest indication that he was not entirely satisfied with his lot.

To his alarm, during his *fortnight's* absence the tribe had almost completed preparations for another attack against Boonesborough. Nearly five hundred warriors had gathered; the ceremonials that preceded a serious warpath were well under way. In the great council house the elders were gathered daily, making their plans, delivering speeches. With each speech the orator presented belts of wampum, one belt for each point he wished to have remembered, generally of white and black; the white made from pieces of the inside of conch shells, the black from mussel shells. Outside the council house the younger men danced around the war post and struck their tomahawks into it, while the women, crooning, patted the drums in rhythm. For three days they would fast, drinking only the war drink of bitter herbs and roots. During that

time no warrior could sit down, or even lean against anything, until after sunset. They had already prepared corn and maple sugar, the only food for the journey. Certain men would control these and parcel them out *rigorously* to the others. No one would touch a mouthful of anything, either of the supplies carried or of the provisions *procured* on the way, except by permission of these men. The waterproof gun-covers of *loons*' skins were in place. The war budget was made up: a bag containing some one article from each man, the skin of a snake, the tail of a buffalo, a martin skin, a bird skin, or what not. On the march this budget would always be carried at the very head of the file by a *designated* official. When the party halted, the budget was laid on the ground, and no one was permitted to pass ahead of it without authority. This was as a measure of discipline. There were other *prohibitions*, too, all of them practical: no one was allowed to lay his pack on a log, and no one was to talk about women or home. And there were other rigid ceremonies on the warpath: for example, when a beast was killed for food, its heart was cut

small and burned on a special fire, and nobody must step across this fire nor go around it except in the direction of the sun. Then when the time came for attack, the budget was opened and its contents distributed to their owners, who attached the articles to the part of the body established by tradition for each. After the battle the budget was reassembled, and the man who took the first scalp now had the privilege of carrying it. After the return, he could *suspend* it before his door for one month — a great honor.

Promptly at the end of the three days of fasting Boone knew that the war party would set forth, no matter what the weather. It was a bad *omen* otherwise. In single file, at spaced intervals, the painted warriors would move from the town, firing their rifles slowly one after the other, beginning at the front and progressing shot by shot to the rear. Once out of hearing of the town, however, a rigid silence was *imposed*. Now the expedition was launched for success or failure. Nothing could interfere with it unless someone had an unfavorable dream, or unless a certain species of bird came and sang near an encampment. This bird the Indians called the Kind Messenger because it brought them warning that the expedition was not lucky. In either of the cases mentioned they always turned back unquestioningly.

Boone knew that his time was short and that if he were to act, it must be at once. No longer could he afford to wait for what he might consider a favorable moment. He took part in the councils and the war dance; he even gave the warriors a few practical suggestions, which they approved. Not by word or look did he indicate that he was anything but pleased at the turn affairs had taken. He had completely deceived the Indians. On the morning of June fifteenth they doled out what they considered the day's supply of ammunition and sent him out to kill deer for the war party. Boone pouched also the powder and half bullets he had been so long accumulating, and struck out boldly across country for home.

There could hardly have been a more unfavorable time to attempt an escape. Five hundred warriors, trained to the minute, were gathered; provisions were prepared. Boone knew that the instant they discovered his flight the whole pack would be on his trail. They knew the country thoroughly, with all its routes and also all its difficulties and *obstructions*. The course he must take would lead through forests and swamps, and across many rivers. If captured he could expect nothing but torture, for the Indians could not fail to see in this attempt a deadly insult, and he now possessed many of their secrets and plans. His only advantage was his certainty of a few hours' start.

His absence was discovered more quickly than he had hoped, however. The entire town was in a rage. Immediately the *fleetest* runners and the keenest hunters scattered themselves through the forest, while others began to puzzle out his trail, and still others loped off on what was considered his probable route. They guessed well. Boone was sorely pressed. He had to use his every art of woodcraft. He doubled and twisted and ran, traveling day and night, almost without rest, until he reached the Ohio River. He dared not fire his gun, so his stored ammunition was of no use to him. He dared not kindle a fire. He dared not spend time searching for even the poor food the barks and roots *afforded* him. Time and again his keen-eyed foes were all about him, but time and again he slipped through them. At length he pushed the bushes cautiously aside and looked out across the reaches of the Ohio River.

The river was swollen by the rains, and its current swept by at mill-race speed. Even the strongest swimmer might well have despaired at this sight, and Boone was not a good swimmer. He had no time to cut a log and trust to the slow and uncertain process of kicking himself across, for the Indians were by now almost at his heels. He descended to the shore, and there he found an old canoe that, after going adrift at some unknown point far upstream, had grounded here at his very feet to answer his great need! And out of all the hundreds of miles of the river course he had picked out this one point at which to *emerge*! Do you wonder that his simple faith was strong that he was "ordained by God to conquer the wilderness"?

The canoe had a hole in it, but Boone managed to make quick repairs of a sort good enough to get him across, though with some difficulty. Once on the other side he felt safe enough to shoot and cook a wild turkey, the only food he tasted in his flight. One meal in five days; one hundred and sixty miles on one meal!

He arrived at Boonesborough *emaciated*, *gaunt*, almost exhausted. The settlers greeted him enthusiastically, but he had to meet a great disappointment, for he had long since been given up as lost, and Rebecca Boone had gathered the remnants of her family and returned to Carolina. Boone speaks of his disappointment, and incidentally shows the great affection that existed between them. "Oppressed," said he, "with the distress of the country and bereaved of me, her only happiness, she had undertaken her long and perilous journey through the wilderness."

It would have been natural, after *recuperating*, for him to follow her, and most men would have done so; but Boone, as usual, put his duty first. As he had feared, the fort was in great need of repair. At once he set the inhabitants *vigorously* to work, and within ten days they had renewed the stockades, built new bastions, replenished the stores of provisions and water, and made everything ready to resist an attack.

THINKING IT THROUGH

1. What instances show that people had confidence in what Daniel Boone said?
2. Why did both Indians and white men trust him so completely?
3. What can you do to cause people to have confidence in your word?
4. Self-discipline means making yourself do the things you ought to do instead of the things you want to do. One who puts duty first, as Daniel Boone did, never considers what he *wants* to do in life but rather what he *ought* to do. What things did Daniel Boone do that he probably did not enjoy? Why did he do them?
5. In what ways did Boone's dedication to duty help others?
6. How did self-discipline help him to survive in the Indian camp? on his dangerous journey home?
7. How has reading about Daniel Boone helped you?
8. After doing research on this incident in Boone's life, write the ending to this story.

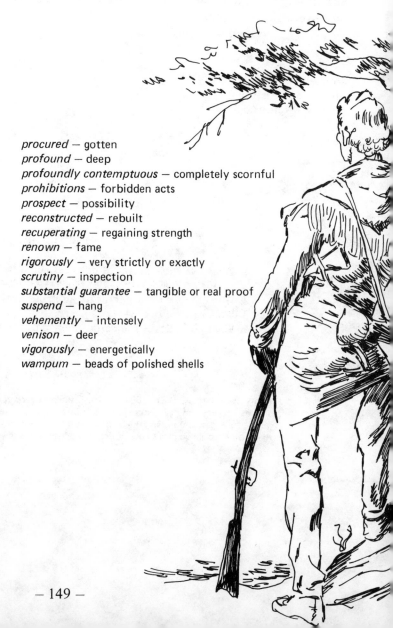

accumulate — gather
acutely — severely
afforded — could give
appalling — alarming
celebrated — famous
clemency — mercy
commodity — product
consulted — asked for their opinion
cordiality — heartiness
declined — refused
designated — chosen
exterior — outward appearance
extraordinary — remarkable
emaciated — very thin and feeble
emerge — come out
fleetest — fastest
fortnight's — two weeks
garments — clothes
garrison — troops
gaunt — weakened by weariness
gravity — dignity
implicitly — unquestioningly
imposed — established
insipid — tasteless
loath — reluctant
loon — a fish-eating, diving bird
merest — smallest
monotonous — tiresome; tedious
necessities — needs
negotiation — conference
obligations — bonds or duties
obstructions — obstacles
omen — sign
probabilities — probable events

procured — gotten
profound — deep
profoundly contemptuous — completely scornful
prohibitions — forbidden acts
prospect — possibility
reconstructed — rebuilt
recuperating — regaining strength
renown — fame
rigorously — very strictly or exactly
scrutiny — inspection
substantial guarantee — tangible or real proof
suspend — hang
vehemently — intensely
venison — deer
vigorously — energetically
wampum — beads of polished shells

PURITY OF CHARACTER

—Henry Ward Beecher

Over the plum and apricot there may be seen a bloom and beauty more exquisite than the fruit itself,—a soft, delicate flush that over-spreads its blushing cheek. Now, if you strike your hand over that and it is once gone, it is gone forever; for it never grows but once. The flower that hangs in the morning, impearled with dew, *arrayed* with jewels,—once shake it so that the beads roll off, and you may sprinkle water over it as you please, yet it can never be made again what it was when the dew fell lightly upon it from heaven.

On a frosty morning you may see the panes of glass covered with landscapes, mountains, lakes, and trees, blended in a beautiful fantastic picture. Now, lay your hand upon the glass, and by the scratch of your fingers, or by the warmth of the palm, all the delicate tracery will be immediately *obliterated.* So in youth there is a *purity* of character which, when once touched and defiled, can never be *restored,*—a fringe more delicate than frostwork, and which, when torn and broken, will never be re-embroidered.

A man who has spotted and soiled his garments in youth, though he may seek to make them white again, can never wholly do it, even were he to wash them with his tears. When a young man leaves his father's house, with the blessing of his mother's tears still wet upon his forehead, if he once loses that early purity of character, it is a loss he can never make whole again. Such is the *consequence* of crime. Its effects cannot be *eradicated,* they can only be forgiven.

arrayed — dressed
obliterated — destroyed
restored — returned

purity — spotless, stainless
consequence — result
eradicated — erased

THINKING IT THROUGH

1. What intangible aspect of our lives could be compared with the "flush on the plum and apricot, the dew on a flower"?
2. Why can't we replace these things in our lives to their original beauty?
3. What can mar our lives?
4. What principles or standards will help us have a strong character?

ABOUT THE AUTHOR

Henry Ward Beecher (1813-1887) became well-known both in the field of literary achievements and as a clergyman. His oratorical mastery contained intense emotion, eloquent drama and picturesque description, sprinkled throughout with humor. He spoke with such force of power that many acclaimed him to be the greatest orator of his day.

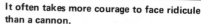

ROSS CARSON'S COURAGE
Author Unknown

We often think that courage is doing something brave;
but sometimes courage is refraining from action.
Read this story to see both kinds of courage in the life of Ross Carson.

Shouting, laughing, pushing against each other, the boys rushed out of the schoolhouse pell-mell.

"Look out, Ross Carson," shouted Tom Lane, in a tone of pretended alarm, "there's a spider on the fountain handle. Run, quick, it may bite you."

There was a roar of laughter at this would-be witty remark, and the eyes of a score or more of thoughtless boys were bent upon the figure of a slender, delicate-looking lad who had been one of the first to get out, and who had approached the fountain for the purpose of getting a drink.

His face flushed painfully as Tom's jest fell on his ear, and the hand that held the handle trembled *perceptibly*, and his lips scarcely touched the water.

"Oh, he'll stand anything rather than double up his little fist," cried Tom, and, crowding close to Ross, he deliberately knocked the books from under his arm. The slender lad's face flushed at the insult, but he said nothing. He stooped, picked the books up, and then walked on again.

He was quite aware of Tom Lane's great *anxiety* to pick a quarrel with him, but was determined to give him no excuse for doing so. For Ross knew that he could not with safety enter into any trial of strength with a boy so much older than himself. His lungs were weak, and the doctor had said they could bear no strain whatever. But it was hard to be called a coward, to bear insults of every description without open *resentment*, to feel that he was looked upon with *contempt* by his companions, because no taunts or sneers could *induce* him to fight. And he was too sensitive and shy to explain to them his reasons for not doing so, knowing well that his explanation would be greeted with ridicule and laughter. So he bore his various trials in silence, and not even his mother knew what he endured.

He did not know that this forbearance showed that he possessed true heroism, for, like most boys, he had a strong admiration for deeds of daring and saw little *merit* in silent endurance.

Tom Lane was the most daring boy among them all. He boasted that he had the coolest head, the strongest arm, and the greatest amount of courage of any fellow of his age in Hillsboro; and none *disputed* his claim. He was always ready for a fight, and generally came off victor in any contest. He had no pity for weakness, no charity for timidity, and thought all those who feared him fair game for his powers of teasing. Ross might have been fairly treated by the other students but for Tom, who was never weary of exciting enmity against him, and, understanding how to magnify the smallest trifles, was always showing him up as "the biggest coward in Hillsboro Academy."

But *retribution* was near at hand.

A new town-hall was being built in Hillsboro; and a very high, imposing *edifice* it was to be, with a steeple second to none. Tom Lane heard his father, who was the contractor for the building, say that a magnificent view could be obtained from this half-completed steeple, and the next day, at the noon recess, Tom proposed to half a dozen of his young friends to go up and take a look for themselves.

"I have a pass from father," he said, "and the carpenters won't make any fuss."

The *ascent* to the steeple was easily made, for narrow, winding stairs led up to it; and the boys soon attained a height that made their heads swim as they looked down, breathless, and saw how small appeared the people on the pavement below.

"A good place for a suicide," said Tom as he leaned out.

"Do be careful," said a low voice, in a tone of *entreaty*, and, looking around, the boys saw Ross Carson standing near. He had come up the stairs *unperceived*.

"How came you here, you little coward?" asked Tom.

"The carpenter gave me leave to come up," answered Ross, quietly. "I did not know any one was up here, and I was anxious to see the view. But it is a dangerous place."

"It's likely you think so," sneered Tom. "You'd find the head of a barrel a dangerous place. As for me, I'd like to see the place where I wouldn't go! Boys, do you see that?"

He pointed to a scaffolding which had been erected about the steeple for the use of the workmen. It projected several feet, and overhung the vast chasm below.

"We see it; but what of it?" asked Louis Raymond.

"You'll see what of it," answered Tom. "It's a jolly place to dance a hornpipe." And before his companions could realize his intention, he had climbed out upon the scaffolding and was walking fearlessly about it.

The boys stared in sheer amazement at such recklessness, and begged him to be careful. Their fears for his safety only made Tom more anxious to show his boasted courage, and he began rather a feeble imitation of a sailor's hornpipe.

"Wouldn't it be a long jump to the pavement?" he said.

As he spoke, he looked down, a fatal thing; for his head, which had until now been so cool and steady, began to whirl strangely. He could not remove his eyes from the awful chasm below him. It seemed to fascinate him.

The boys looked at each other in horror. They saw the terrible danger which *menaced* him. He stood in a kind of stupor, looking down into the fascinating gulf, his eyes wild and staring, his face white with terror. He, too, knew the awful danger in which he stood, but he was powerless to help himself. The slightest change of position, even the raising of his eyes, and he would fall. The gulf seemed to be drawing him on; his brain grew more *torpid* with every instant, and his eyes seemed started from their sockets. Back of him shuddered his horror-stricken comrades waiting in an agony of suspense for the fatal end of this terrible drama. Before and below him yawned the great chasm, at the bottom of which the people moving along looked like dwarfs.

Suddenly there was a movement among the boys, and Ross Carson, with white face and set teeth, climbed quickly and noiselessly out of the steeple onto the scaffolding, and with steady step approached the boy who stood on the brink of such a fearful death.

"If he touches him Tom will fall," whispered Louis Raymond.

Low as the whisper was, Ross heard it, and half turned his head toward Louis, pausing an instant, as if to think. Then he made a quick, firm step forward, and throwing both arms around Tom's waist, dragged him backward.

It was all over in an instant. In the face of a fearful and *imminent* danger, Ross saved his enemy, and slowly, carefully, for every step was *peril*, drew him back to the steeple, and with the help of the other boys got him inside once more, white as a corpse, it is true, and utterly unnerved, but safe.

There was little said by any one. In silence Ross helped Tom *descend* the winding stair, and then walked home as quickly as possible.

"I don't feel well enough to go to school again this afternoon," he said to his mother, "so I'll weed out your flower beds for you."

"You are pale," said Mrs. Carson. "I'm afraid you study too hard."

Ross did not answer, but threw off his coat and began to weed the beds, hoping by hard work to overcome the nervousness which had possessed him ever since leaving the new town hall. He was still weeding a couple of hours later, when he heard the tramp of many feet, and, looking up, he saw about a dozen of his schoolmates, coming in at the little wooden gate, Tom Lane first of all.

"I've come to ask your forgiveness, Ross Carson," said Tom, holding out his hand. "You've taught me this day what true courage is, and made me see what a cowardly sneak I've been."

Tom's lips quivered as he made this humiliating confession, and his eyes were moist with the tears which he could *restrain* with only the greatest effort. Ross took the proffered hand in a warm and hearty grasp as he said: "I'd have done as much for any one Tom. Don't make so much of it. But I'm out and out glad to be friends with you."

And friends, fast and true, they were from that time forth; and no one ever again even whispered that Ross Carson lacked courage.

anxiety — desire
ascent — climb
contempt — dislike
descend — walk down
edifice — building
entreaty — pleading
imminent — immediate
induce — force
menaced — threatened
merit — manly virtue
perceptibly — so as to be seen
peril — danger
resentment — displeasure
restrain — hold back; prevent
retribution — a return for something suffered
torpid — numb
unperceived — unseen

THINKING IT THROUGH

1. How did Ross Carson show true courage when the boys insulted him?
2. Do you think it took more courage to remain silent than to speak or act in anger? Why?
3. Later Ross proves that he is very brave. How?
4. What is a bully? Is a bully really courageous? Was Tom as brave as he thought he was? Explain your answer.
5. Bullies talk and act big only when they are in a group; a brave person can stand alone anywhere. Bring a newspaper article which illustrates this principle.
6. Name several ways Ross proved that he possessed strong, noble character.
7. What was the one brave thing Tom did?

YOUR REPUTATION

— J. L. Nichols

Learn to be a man of your word. One of the most disheartening of all things is to be *compelled* to do business with a person whose promise is not to be depended upon. There are plenty of people in this wide world whose promise is as slender a tie as a spider's web. Let your given word be as a *hempen* cord, a chain of wrought steel that will bear the heaviest strain. It will go far in making a man of you, and a real man is the noblest work of God. The man who does not honorably meet his promises is not only dishonest but is also a coward; the man who dares not meet his *obligations* in good faith can frame no other excuse than that of cowardice.

Young man, have a character of your own. Do not be a lump of moist putty molded and shaped by the influence and impressions of those whom you last met. Your reputation is made up by your conduct. Cultivate force, energy, self-reliance and be a positive quantity that can be counted upon at all times and at all places. Be a man whose word is worth a hundred cents on a dollar and your reputation will be as good as gold.

compelled — forced
hempen — tough fiber used for rope
obligations — duties

THINKING IT THROUGH

1. Explain the following quotes: (a) "There are plenty of people . . . whose promise is as slender a tie as a spider's web." (b) "Let your word be as a hempen cord, a chain of wrought steel . . . "
2. How is your reputation made?
3. The author states, "Do not be a lump of moist putty molded and shaped by the influence and impressions of those you last met." What does he mean and how can you avoid this weakness?

A NATION'S STRENGTH
— Ralph Waldo Emerson

Not gold, but only man can make
    A people great and strong;
Men who, for truth and honor's sake,
    Stand fast and suffer long.

Brave men who work while others sleep,
    Who dare while others fly —
They build a nation's pillars deep
    And lift them to the sky.

One man who left "footprints on the sands of time"
is Thomas A. Edison.
Though this extraordinary American died in 1931, his work continues
to bless the world in countless ways today.

THOMAS EDISON

by B. C. Forbes

You and I often think of inventors as geniuses who suddenly are hit by a brilliant idea from out of the air and immediately patent it in workable form. We picture them as *eccentric* fellows who for the most part sit around waiting for a stroke of inspiration.

Edison was not of that type. He angrily resented being called a genius or a wizard or a magician. "Genius is one percent inspiration and 99 percent perspiration," he declared. "The three great essentials to achieve anything worth while are: first, hard work; second, stick-to-itiveness; third, common sense."

Edison is acclaimed as the world's greatest inventor. After he had achieved success as an inventor and manufacturer, he deliberately dropped everything else and adopted invention for his profession and life work in 1876. After that he simply had to make good or become a laughingstock. Edison made good.

He was also the world's greatest experimenter. He tried thousands and thousands of ways—sometimes fifty thousand—to do a thing and never quit, even if it should take ten years, until he had either found a way or proved *conclusively* that it could not be done.

Edison worked harder and slept less than any other great man in history - - he once worked continuously, without a moment's sleep, for five days and nights, while per-

fecting the phonograph. He conducted more experiments than any other human being. He took out upward of 100 patents in one year and secured a grand total of over 1,000 patents, a record unapproached by any other individual in this country or abroad.

He tasted the bitterest defeats and lost all his money time and again. He spent five solid years and over $2,000,000 creating a plan and a plant to extract ores by magnets from powdered rock, only to find that the discovery of unlimited quantities of rich Mesaba ore made his whole process profitless and it had to be abandoned, leaving him grievously in debt, but unbroken in spirit.

Difficulties which would drive normal *mortals* to despair only lighted up Edison's enthusiasm and *stimulated* his determination to triumph. If a thing wouldn't work one way, he tried it another way - - 5,000 other ways, 10,000 other ways, 20,000 other ways, if necessary. He sent *botanists*, mineralogists, chemists, *geologists*, and others into the most *remote*, uncivilized nooks of the earth in search of some fiber or other elusive material which the indefatigable experimenter calculated might prove the missing link in a chain of experiments - - one expert *circumscribed* the globe in search of a species of bamboo which Edison figured might supply just the right filament for his in-the-making incandescent lamp, while other explorers combed South America for a fiber which might still better serve the purpose.

He had a philosophy of failure which all of us might well adopt. If after thousands of attempts, the expenditure of hundreds of thousands of dollars, and apparent waste of precious years, he had only failure for his reward, he did not complain, he did not feel downcast. When his assistants *commiserat-*

ed with him and themselves on the *futility* of all their pains, Edison would cheerfully *reprimand* them thus: "Our work has not been in vain; our experiments have taught us a lot. We have added something to the total of human knowledge. We have demonstrated that it cannot be done. Isn't that something? Now let's take up the next thing."

That was Edison. He didn't waste time and *vitality* bemoaning the past when the present and the future were calling so loudly to have great and small things accomplished. He looked forward, not backward.

Edison's philosophy was reflected in his life. A minister once asked him, "What are the greatest safeguards against temptation?" Edison replied, "If I were to *hazard* a guess as to what young people should do to avoid temptation it would be to get a job and work at it so hard that temptation would not exist for them."

Edison always sought to produce things that would benefit mankind. Has any other person added so much to the comfort, enjoyment, enrichment of the lives of his fellow mortals? Edison stretched out his hand, seized hold of the fleeting sounds of the human voice, and made them imperishable by means of the recording machine. He captured motion with his invention of moving pictures; he helped to send sound across continents and oceans by his early achievements in telephony; he flooded the world with electric light.

In *evolving* his incandescent lamp Edison ransacked the earth for suitable materials.

He tested 6,000 vegetable growths brought from all parts of the globe in his search for an ideal substance for use as a filament inside the glass bulb. At first he used a piece of carbonized cotton thread, later he found that a certain kind of bamboo yielded a better fiber, but finally he discarded all carbon filaments in favour of metallic ones.

Edison's task in inventing and establishing the first electric lighting plant in New York in September, 1882, was immense. It involved not only the construction of absolutely new forms of machinery and apparatus, but it also involved the problems of laying the necessary wires, of originating methods and apparatus for regulating and subdividing the current, or *inducing* people to agree to the installment of the little-tested invention, and of answering a thousand questions never faced before. The immensity of this burden cannot be grasped today when a generation of experience and familiarity with electric lighting has led us to accept everything pertaining to it as a matter of course. At the end of 1882, only 225 buildings in New York had been wired, including the offices of *J. P. Morgan*, who became one of Edison's admirers and supporters. For three months the current was supplied free to those brave enough to allow their places to be threaded with the mysterious wires which, it was feared, might start fires or cause explosions at any moment.

The story of the multiple-arc system, of the revolutionary three-wire system which saved 60 per cent of the copper formerly used, the introduction of central stations in spite of all opposition and ignorance, the invention of a meter for measuring consumption of the current - - this story of the birth of a new era in human progress is too full of incident to permit its being even outlined here. It is enough to say that Thomas A. Edison's accomplishments in this field stamped him the greatest inventive figure of the age.

Electric railway experiments next arrested Edison's chief attention, and by using track for a circuit, he achieved wonderful results. He built an electric line at Menlo Park, New Jersey, which attracted railroad builders and engineers from all parts of the

world; but somehow they were not so quick as Edison to grasp the possibilities of the field thus opened up.

There followed Edison's *epochal* inventions for the manufacture of cement - - half the Portland cement produced in America was later made in Edison kilns. In one day of almost twenty-four hours, Edison personally prepared detailed plans for his first cement plant, covering a length of half a mile, a feat regarded by experts as the most stupendous ever performed by a human brain in one day. From the manufacture of cement to the pouring of cement houses was a logical step - - and, incidentally, Edison believed this method of construction was only in its infancy.

In his late years the electric storage battery wireless apparatus, the Edison-Sims torpedo and other submarine problems, improvements in the phonograph, the dictating machine, the inventing of speaking motion pictures, and household labor-saving devices claimed most of the master inventor's time and talent. Thomas Edison, America's greatest inventor, left us a legacy, not only of material conveniences, but also of the value of perseverance, dedication, and service.

THINKING IT THROUGH

1. What were Edison's three essentials for achievement?
2. What advice did he give to help young people avoid temptation?
3. Someone had said that the best use one can make of his life is to spend it for something that will live after it. How is this true of Edison?
4. What can you do that will have not just temporal, but eternal, value?

botanists — a specialist in the study of plants
circumscribed — circled
commiserated — sympathized
conclusively — beyond a doubt
eccentric — strange
epochal — a time characterized by a distinctive development
evolving — developing
futility — uselessness
geologists — a specialist in the study of rocks
hazard — venture
incandescent lamp — an electric lamp in which a filament gives off light when heated to intense heat by an electric current

indefatigable — untiring
inducing — persuading
J. P. Morgan — an American financier
mortals — people
remote — distant
reprimand — rebuke
species — kind
stimulated — aroused
stupendous — astonishing
vitality — strength

THEODORE ROOSEVELT

Author Unknown

Few men have been as popular as Theodore Roosevelt. There was something in his wonderful sympathy that appealed to everyone who knew him and to the millions who could only read about him. Like Lincoln, he loved the common people. Lincoln said, "the Lord must love common people because he made so many of them." Neither of these two great leaders set himself apart from the great mass of people. When they spoke, the people recognized the voice of real friends.

"I am a sounding board," Roosevelt used to say. "How can I help in this good cause?" Truly he was a sounding board that, before the days of radio, echoed throughout the land. Crooked deals fled before his *denunciation*; corrupt leaders were driven from office; clean young men were encouraged to take part in political life.

A study of the lives of the great men of the world shows hardly one able to do as many different things supremely well as Theodore Roosevelt. He was one of the most forceful and convincing public speakers of his day. He wrote many books that are still read with keenest interest. He was a thorough student of nature and loved all outdoor life. When he was leading his regiment in Cuba during the Spanish War, he astonished his officers by naming rare birds in the jungles. He was a successful soldier, a skillful politician, one of our greatest presidents, and, more important, an example of righteous living to all the millions of people in our country.

denunciation — strong condemnation of evil

THINKING IT THROUGH

1. How were Abraham Lincoln and Theodore Roosevelt alike?
2. The author says that crooked deals fled before his denunciation. What does this mean?

Beautiful thoughts make beautiful memories. If you will have happy memories, you must be constantly storing happy times in your heart. Form the habit of looking for the beautiful in life, and you are sure to find it.
As James Whitcomb Riley turns the warm, happy pages of memory we too, enjoy going "out to Old Aunt Mary's."

OUT TO OLD AUNT MARY'S
— James Whitcomb Riley

Wasn't it pleasant, O brother mine,
In those old days of the lost sunshine
Of youth — when the Saturday's chores were through
And the "Sunday's wood" in the kitchen, too,
And we went visiting, "me and you."
    Out to Old Aunt Mary's —

It all comes back so clear to-day!
Though I am as bald as you are gray,—
Out by the barn-lot and down the lane
We patter along in the dust again,
As light as the tips of the drops of the rain,
    Out to Old Aunt Mary's

We cross the pastures, and through the wood,
Where the old gray snag of the poplar stood,
Where the hammering "red-heads" hopped awry,
And the buzzard "raised" in the "clearing" sky
And lolled and circled, as we went by
    Out to Old Aunt Mary's

And then in the dust of the road again;
And the teams we met, and the countrymen;
And the long highway, with sunshine spread
As thick as butter on country bread,
Our cares behind, and our hearts ahead
    Out to Old Aunt Mary's —

Why, I see her now in the open door
Where the little gourds grew up the sides and o'er
The clapboard roof! — And her face — ah, me!
Wasn't it good for a boy to see —
And wasn't it good for a boy to be
    Out to Old Aunt Mary's? —

The jelly — the jam and the marmalade,
And the cherry — and quince — "preserves" she made!
And the sweet-sour pickles of peach and pear,
With cinnamon in 'em, and all things rare! —
And the more we ate was the more to spare,
    Out to Old Aunt Mary's.

Ah! was there, ever, so kind a face
And gentle as hers, or such a grace
Of welcoming, as she cut the cake
Or the juicy pies that she joyed to make
Just for the visiting children's sake —
    Out to Old Aunt Mary's?

The honey, too, in its amber comb
One finds only in an old farm-home;
And the coffee, fragrant and sweet, and oh!
So hot that we gloried to drink it so,
With spangles of tears in our eyes, you know —
    Out to Old Aunt Mary's.

And the romps we took, in our glad unrest!
Was it the lawn that we loved the best,
With its swooping swing in the locust trees,
Or was it the grove, with its leafy breeze,
Or the dim hay-mow, with its fragrances —
    Out to Old Aunt Mary's?

And then, in the garden, — near the side
Where the bee-hives were and the path was wide, —
The apple-house — like a fairy cell —
And the little square door we knew so well,
And the wealth inside but our tongues could tell —
    Out to Old Aunt Mary's.

And the old spring-house, in the cool green gloom
Of the willow trees, — and the cooler room
Where the swinging shelves and the crocks were kept,
Where the cream in a golden languor slept,
While the waters gurgled and laughed and wept —
    Out to Old Aunt Mary's.

And as many a time have you and I —
Barefoot boys in the days gone by —
Knelt, and in tremulous ecstasies
Dipped our lips into sweets like these, —
Memory now is on her knees
    Out to Old Aunt Mary's. —

For, O my brother, so far away,
This is to tell you — she waits today
To welcome us: — Aunt Mary fell
Asleep this morning, whispering, "Tell
The boys to come" . . . And all is well
    Out to Old Aunt Mary's.

THE GREAT WERE ONCE AS YOU

-- Edgar A. Guest

The great were once as you.
They whom men magnify today
Once *groped* and blundered on life's way.
Were fearful of themselves, and thought
By magic was men's greatness wrought.
They feared to try what they could do;
Yet Fame hath crowned with her success
The selfsame gifts that you possess.

The great were young as you,
Dreaming the very dreams you hold,
Longing, yet fearing, to be bold,
Doubting that they themselves possessed
The strength and skill for every test,
Uncertain of the truths they knew,
Not sure that they could stand to fate
With all the courage of the great.

Then came a day when they
Their first bold venture made,
Scorning to cry for aid.
They dared to stand to fight alone,
Took up the *gauntlet* life had thrown,
Charged full-front to the gray,
Mastered their fear of self, and then
Learned that our great men are but men.

Oh, Youth, go forth and do!
You, too, to fame may rise;
You can be strong and wise.
Stand up to life and play the man —
You can if you'll but think you can;
THE GREAT WERE ONCE AS YOU.
You envy them their proud success?
'Twas won with gifts that you possess.

groped — to feel about uncertainly
gauntlet — challenge

THE MAXIMS OF POOR RICHARD

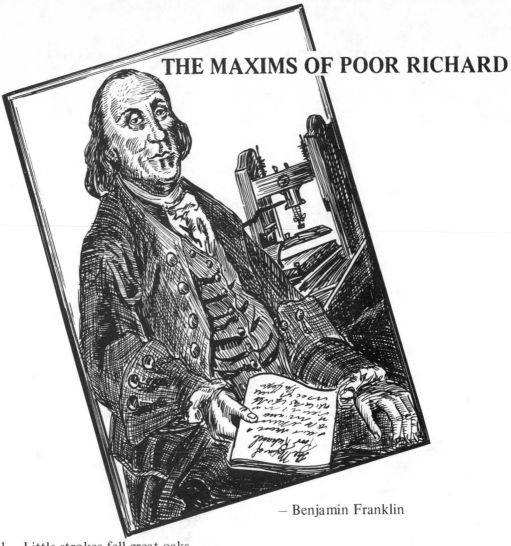

— Benjamin Franklin

1. Little strokes fell great oaks.
2. God helps them that help themselves.
3. The sleeping fox catches no poultry.
4. He that rises late must trot all day.
5. There are no gains without pains.
6. Diligence is the mother of good luck.
7. One to-day is worth two to-morrows.
8. Be ashamed to catch yourself idle.
9. If you would have your business done, go; if not, send.
10. Think of saving as well as of getting.
11. Always taking out of the meal tub and never putting in soon comes to the
    bottom.
12. He that goes a-borrowing goes a-sorrowing.
13. 'Tis hard for an empty bag to stand upright.
14. Experience keeps a dear school, but fools will learn in no other.
15. If you will not hear reason she will surely rap your knuckles.
16. He that can have patience can have what he will.
17. Search others for their virtues, thyself for thy vices.
18. Early to bed and early to rise, Makes a man healthy, wealthy, and wise.
19. Have you somewhat to do to-morrow? Do it today.
20. Constant dropping wears away stones.
21. If you would have a faithful servant and one that you like, serve yourself.
22. Fools make feasts and wise men eat them.
23. If you would know the value of money, go and try to borrow some.

BEN FRANKLIN

FRANKLIN'S LESSON ON THE VALUE OF TIME

- Author Unknown

Does thou love life? Then, do not squander time, for that is the stuff life is made of!
—Franklin

Franklin not only understood the value of time, but he put a price upon it that made others appreciate its value.

A customer who came one day to his little bookstore in Philadelphia, not being satisfied with the price demanded by the clerk for the book he wished to purchase, asked for the *proprietor*.

"Mr. Franklin is very busy just now in the pressroom," replied the clerk.

The man, however, who had already spent an hour *aimlessly* turning over books, insisted on seeing him. In answer to the clerk's summons, Mr. Franklin hurried out from the printing office at the back of the store to see what was wanted.

"What is the lowest price you can take for this book, sir?" asked the *leisurely* customer, holding up the volume he had chosen.

"One dollar and a quarter," was the prompt reply.

"A dollar and a quarter! Why, your clerk asked me only a dollar for it just now."

"True," said Franklin, "and I could have better afforded to take a dollar than to leave my work and get a dollar and a quarter."

The man, seemed to be in doubt as to whether Mr. Franklin was in earnest, said coaxingly, "Come now, Mr. Franklin, tell me what is your lowest price for this book."

"One dollar and a half," was the grave reply.

"A dollar and a half! Why, you just offered it to me for a dollar and a quarter."

"Yes, and I could better have taken that price then than a dollar and a half now."

Without another word, the *crestfallen* purchaser laid the money on the counter and left the store with his book. He had learned not only that he who *squanders* his own time is foolish, but that he who wastes the time of others is a thief.

proprietor — owner
aimlessly — without purpose

leisurely — unhurried
crestfallen — humiliated
squanders — wastes

Benjamin Franklin, noted for his wisdom and humor,
became one of young America's most useful citizens. Throughout this selection
you will find numerous evidences of his quick common sense and inventive genius. Look for
the principles by which he guided his life, and compare
these with the principles by which you guide your life.

Choice, not chance, determines human destiny.

BENJAMIN FRANKLIN

—Mary Lee

When I was a little girl, I used to stand for long minutes at a time in my grandmother's broad front hall, looking up at a picture that hung there on the wall. It was like gazing out of a window from the cool dark of the hall into the bright ballroom of a French palace. There before me was a great room, whose high, arched mirrors reflected vistas of the other rooms beyond. There were rich brocade hangings, and many candles, and a shiny floor that reflected the flowered gowns of the ladies.

For the room was full of lovely ladies—ladies with great, ruffled skirts, ladies with white necks and pretty faces and powdered hair and nodding ostrich plumes. There were gentlemen, too, such fine gentlemen, in coats of embroidered velvet and richly flowered waistcoats, with ruffles of lace at their wrists, and swords at their belts, and neat, powdered wigs on their heads, and cocked hats under their arms. And all of this gay company were looking in one direction. They were looking toward a short, stout man, a simple, grandfatherly man, dressed plainly in black, with no sword, no cocked hat, no lace ruffles, no wig on his head, but his own gray hair brushed back from a broad, fine forehead. One lovely lady had raised her white arm above this simple man, and was about to lay a laurel wreath on his head. Another lady on his other side was offering him, very reverently, a bouquet of roses, while all the gay courtiers of the King of France looked on.

Who was this short, stout man, so plainly dressed, about whom all these magnificent people were making such a fuss? I used to stand on my tiptoes and read the letters engraved there under the picture: BENJAMIN FRANKLIN AT THE COURT OF FRANCE. The plain citizen of a new, strange, young country at the court of an old, civilized, powerful country. Much later, I found out why it was that so plain a man should win such great respect at the most brilliant court of all Europe.

When Benjamin Franklin was a boy, living with his father and mother in Boston, his father used to repeat to him the proverb of Solomon: "Seest thou a man *diligent* in his calling, he shall stand before kings, he shall not stand before mean men." Benjamin Franklin was a poor boy; he started out in life with only two years of schooling, and with no money in his pocket, but with this principle that his father had taught him of diligence. It was this principle that made him one of the most *eminent* men in our country, and he did at last stand before five different kings.

Franklin was born in 1706 in Boston. When he was eight years old he went to the grammar school there. Two years later he became his father's assistant in a candle-making shop. Two years after that he became an apprentice to his brother, who printed a newspaper. While he was working for his brother, he wrote articles for the paper, and also wrote ballads, printed them, and sold them on the streets. All the time, Franklin studied languages, and practiced writing good English by copying the fine style of Joseph Addison, a famous English writer of the time, in the Spectator. In 1723 he left Boston and went to Philadelphia.

It was a cold October night when this youth of seventeen landed at the old Market Street *wharf* in Philadelphia. He was poorly dressed, his pockets stuffed out with shirts and stockings, and all his other possessions in a little bundle in his hand.

He bought himself three great puffy rolls of bread, and eating one of them, he walked up the street. In one of the doorways there stood a young girl who noticed this strange-looking boy, eating his roll as he walked. The girl was Miss Deborah Reed, who afterward married Franklin.

Some day, in the book that Franklin wrote for his little son, you may read how he obtained work in a printer's office; how he went back to Boston on a visit and was forgiven by his father for running away; and how he went to England and worked in printing offices there. You will read how he returned to Philadelphia and started a printing office of his own; how he edited and printed a newspaper; how he became a member of the Assembly, and Deputy Postmaster General, and Commissioner to treat with the Indians; and how he filled other important offices. And you will read about Poor Richard's Almanac, which Franklin published, and which contained many maxims and proverbs and *sage* sayings, but more than anything else encouraged thrift and industry.

"Sloth makes all things difficult, but industry all things easy," Poor Richard says. "He that riseth late must trot all day, and shall scarce overtake his business at night; while laziness travels so slowly that poverty soon overtakes him. Drive thy business! let not that drive thee!"

"Early to bed and early to rise
Makes a man healthy, wealthy, and wise."

"So what signifies wishing and hoping for better times? We may make these times better if we bestir ourselves. There are no gains without pains."

"Then plough deep while sluggards sleep, And you shall have corn to sell and keep."

"If you were a servant, would you not be ashamed that a good master should catch you idle? Are you, then, your own master? Be ashamed to catch yourself *idle.*"

"We must add *frugality,* if we would make our industry more certainly successful."

"Great estates may venture more, But little boats should keep near shore."

diligent — industrious
eminent — outstanding
wharf — dock

sage — wise
idle — lazy
frugality — thrift

Franklin set himself a great task—to study everything about him and learn how it worked and how it might work better than it did; and also to inquire into his own conscience and learn in every way how to prune away the faults he found there and to make himself stronger-souled each day. He planned for himself a regular program of self-searching, but when he became discouraged at faults which cropped up while he was watching to nip off others, he acknowledged that no one could be absolutely perfect, and decided quaintly that he should let some little faults remain, anyhow, "to keep his friends in countenance!" So you see he was very, very human, and knew how to understand other people because he knew himself so well.

Here are some of the things that Benjamin Franklin accomplished in the seventy-nine years before he was summoned to meet great kings.

He discovered that lightning is electricity, which nobody knew before. He proved his theory by an experiment with a key tied to a kite. He invented lightning rods, to carry the electricity away from houses. He was the first to discover that an electric current running through a wire that is wound around a piece of steel will magnetize the piece of steel. Because of this discovery other men have been able to invent the telegraph, the telephone, and the electric motor.

In some old-fashioned houses you may see a queer kind of open stove, like a little iron fireplace, set out into the room and connected with the chimney by a stove-pipe. People will tell you that this is a Franklin stove, the first successful stove for burning wood. He believed that if the fire could be brought out into the room, much of the heat that had been wasted up the chimney could be used. This was his thrifty thought; and so he made his iron fireplace, all open in the front for the merry flames, and this was the first stove. Then he invented a way to get rid of smoke from the stoves, and from the chimneys; and while he was at it he found a way to make

a street light that did not smoke. At that time even in London the streets were dark because the lamps were always smoky. One thing led to another; he stopped the smoke in the street lamps, then he organized the first street-cleaning department.

He reached out further and found other ways for civic betterment. He established the first successful circulating library, the first academy, the first hospital in the city of Philadelphia, and he founded the University of Pennsylvania.

He saw the need of protection against losses by fire, and helped to establish the first insurance company of America. And he founded the postal service in the United States and was the first Postmaster General.

Larger and larger grew his field of service. He pointed out the advantage of building ships with watertight compartments, which all large modern ships now use. He was the first to recognize the fact that the Gulf Stream is warmer than the water on each side of it, and the first to make a chart of the direction and course of the Gulf Stream. And he was the first to show that oil poured on stormy waters will still heavy waves. This scientific truth has come to be a symbol for bringing peace out of disturbance—when you hear it said that someone is pouring oil on troubled waters, it means that the person is a peacemaker.

Franklin himself, the eminent scientist, successful editor, practical inventor, poured oil on the troubled waters of politics and was a great statesman and a great diplomat. He was the only one of the early patriots who signed all four of the great State papers that gave the United States its national existence: the Declaration of Independence, the Treaty of Alliance with France, the Treaty of Peace with England, and the Constitution of the United States.

And this frugal, earnest, great man found time to think of little things to make life easier. He invented spectacles for near-sighted and farsighted eyes, and made a pair which he wore himself. He made the first mangle for smoothing washed clothes—George Washington watched a demonstration of this machine. He invented a copying press for duplicating letters written with ink. He drew the first newspaper cartoon; he was the first to print pictures in a paper and to publish questions and answers. He helped to establish eighteen paper mills in America.

In the picture that hung in my grandmother's broad hall, there he was, a short, stout man, a simple, grandfatherly man, with no sword and no ruffles and no wig, looking *benignly* and with humor, through the iron-rimmed spectacles he had made himself, at the gay company doing him *homage*—Benjamin Franklin at the Court of France.

When Thomas Jefferson was sent to France in 1785, the French Minister of Foreign Affairs said, "You replace Dr. Franklin, I hear?"

"I succeed him," said Jefferson. "No one can replace him."

benignly — gently, kindly
homage — honor

THINKING IT THROUGH

The principle of diligence Benjamin Franklin learned as a boy stayed with him and led him to become an unusually successful and useful person even though he started out poor and with little schooling.

1. Franklin's writings are filled with wise sayings about thrift and industry. How did Franklin apply these two virtues to himself? How could they help improve our lives?

2. Choose one of his sayings that you would like to make a rule for your life. Write a short essay on its meaning.

3. The author says that as a youth Franklin determined "to study everything about him," "to make himself stronger-souled each day," and to plan "a regular program of self-searching." How did he profit from following these resolutions? How would they help develop character today?

JOIN, or DIE.

Printer's device used by Franklin

BELL OF LIBERTY

Peter Faneuil

There was *tumult* in the city,
   In the quaint old Quaker town,
And the streets were *rife* with people
   Pacing restless up and down;
People gathering at corners,
   Where they whispered each to each,
And the sweat stood on their temples,
   With the earnestness of speech.

As the black Atlantic currents
   Lash the wild Newfoundland shore,
So they beat against the State House,
   So they surged against the door;
And the mingling of their voices
   Made a harmony profound,
Till the quiet street of Chestnut
   Was all turbulent with sound.

"Will they do it?" "Dare they do it?"
   "Who is speaking?" "What's the news?"
"What of Adams?" "What of Sherman?"
   "O, God grant they won't refuse!"
"Make some way, there!" "Let me nearer!"
   "I am stifling!" - "Stifle then:
When a nation's life's at *hazard*,
   We've no time to think of men!"

So they beat against the *portal* —
   Man and woman, maid and child;
And the July sun in heaven
   On the scene looked down and smiled;
The same sun that saw the Spartan
   Shed his patriot blood in vain,
Now beheld the soul of freedom
   All unconquered rise again.

Aloft in that high steeple
   Sat the bellman, old and gray;
He was weary of the tyrant
   And his iron-sceptered sway;
So he sat with one hand ready
   On the clapper of the bell,
When his eye should catch the signal,
   The long expected news to tell.

See! see! the dense crowd quivers
   Through all its lengthy line,
As the boy beside the portal
   Looks forth to give the sign!
With his small hands upward lifted,
   Breezes *dallying* with his hair,
Hark! with deep, clear intonation,
   Breaks his young voice on the air.

Hushed the people's swelling murmur,
   List the boy's strong joyous cry!
"Ring!" he shouts aloud; "RING! Grandpa!
   Ring! O, RING for LIBERTY!"
And straightway, at the signal,
   The old bellman lifts his hand,
And sends the good news, making
   Iron music through the land.

How they shouted! What rejoicing!
   How the old bell shook the air,
Till the clang of freedom ruffled
   The calmly gliding Delaware!
How the bonfires and the torches
   Lighted up the night's repose,
And from the flames, like Phoenix,
   Fair liberty arose!

That old State House bell is silent —
   Hushed is now its clamorous tongue;
But the spirit is awakened
   Still is living — ever young.
And when we greet the sunlight
   On the Fourth of each July,
We will ne'er forget the bellman,
   Who, betwixt the earth and sky,
Rang out our Independence,
   Which, please God, shall never die!

tumult — commotion
rife — crowded
hazard — stake
portal — door
dallying — playing

THE CHILDREN'S SONG

Rudyard Kipling

Land of our birth, we pledge to thee
Our love and toil in the years to be,
When we are grown and take our place,
As men and women with our race.

Father in Heaven who lovest all,
Oh help Thy children when they call;
That they may build from age to age,
An undefiled heritage.

Teach us to bear the yoke in youth,
With steadfastness and careful truth:
That, in our time, Thy Grace may give
The truth whereby the Nations live.

Teach us to rule ourselves alway,
Controlled and cleanly night and day:
That we may bring, if need arise,
No maimed or worthless sacrifice.

Teach us to look in all our ends,
On Thee for judge, and not our friends;
That we, with Thee, may walk uncowed
By fear or favor of the crowd.

Teach us the strength that can not seek
By deed or thought, to hurt the weak;
That, under Thee, we may possess
Man's strength to comfort man's distress.

Teach us delight in simple things,
And *Mirth* that has no bitter springs;
Forgiveness free of evil done,
And love to men 'neath the sun!

Land of our Birth, our Faith, our Pride,
For whose dear sake our fathers died;
O Motherland, we pledge to thee,
Head, heart and hand through the years to be.

Mirth — laughter

THINKING IT THROUGH

1. What is an undefiled heritage?
2. Who does Kipling say can help us to build an undefiled heritage?
3. What does Kipling mean when he says, "Teach us to bear the yoke in youth"?
4. Name ways that you can "bear the yoke in youth."
5. How can you find "delight in simple things"? Describe some simple things you enjoy.
6. Tell the last verse of the poem in your own words.

The humorous deeds and misdeeds of Tom Sawyer transport us to the thrilling
by-gone era of Mississippi Riverboats and quaint, small-town living.
In this chapter of Mark Twain's classic, *The Adventures of Tom Sawyer,*
Tom has a problem and solves it in a unique way.

THE GLORIOUS WHITEWASHER

Mark Twain

Saturday morning was come, and all the summer world was bright and fresh, and brimming with life. There was a song in every heart; and if the heart was young, the music issued at the lips. There was cheer in every face and a spring in every step. The locust trees were in bloom and the fragrance of the blossoms filled the air. Cardiff Hill, beyond the village and above it, was green with vegetation, and it lay just far enough away to seem a *Delectable* Land, dreamy, *reposeful*, and inviting.

Tom appeared on the sidewalk with a bucket of whitewash and a long-handled brush. He *surveyed* the fence, and all gladness left him and a deep *melancholy* settled down upon his spirit. Thirty yards of board fence nine feet high. Life to him seemed hollow, and existence but a burden. Sighing, he dipped his brush and passed it along the topmost plank; repeated the operation; did it again; compared the *insignificant* whitewashed streak with the far-reaching continent of unwhitewashed fence, and sat down

on a tree-box discouraged. Jim came skipping out at the gate with a tin pail, and singing "Buffalo Gals." Bringing water from the town pump had always been hateful work in Tom's eyes before, but now it did not strike him so. He remembered that there was company at the pump. White, mulatto, and Negro boys and girls were always there waiting their turns, resting, trading playthings, quarreling, fighting, skylarking. And he remembered that although the pump was only a hundred and fifty yards off, Jim never got back with a bucket of water under an hour — and even then somebody generally had to go after him. Tom said:

"Say, Jim, I'll fetch the water if you'll whitewash some."

Jim shook his head and said:

"Can't, Mars Tom. Ole missis, she tole me I got to go an' git dis water an' not stop foolin' rqun' wid anybody. She say she spec' Mars Tom gwine to ax me to whitewash, an' so she tole me to go 'long an' 'tend to my business — she 'lowed she'd tend to de whitewashin'."

"Oh, never you mind what she said, Jim. That's the way she always talks. Gimme the bucket — I won't be gone only a minute. She won't ever know."

"Oh, I dasn't, Mars Tom. Ole missis she'd take an' tar de head of'n me. 'Deed she would."

"She! She never licks anybody — whacks 'em over the head with her thimble — and who cares for that, I'd like to know. She talks awful, but talk don't hurt — anyways it don't if she don't cry. Jim, I'll give you a *marvel*. I'll give you a white alley!"

Jim began to waver.

"White alley, Jim! And it's a bully *taw*."

"My! Dat's a mighty gay marvel, I tell you! But Mars Tom I's powerful 'fraid ole missis —"

"And besides, if you will, I'll show you my sore toe."

Jim was only human — this attraction was too much for him. He put down his pail, took the white alley, and bent over the toe with absorbing interest while the bandage was being unwound. In another moment he was flying down the street with his pail and a tingling rear, Tom was whitewashing with vigor, and Aunt Polly was *retiring* from the field with a slipper in her hand and triumph in her eye.

But Tom's energy did not last. He began to think of the fun he had planned for this day, and his sorrows multiplied. Soon the free boys would come tripping along on all sorts of delicious expeditions, and they would make a world of fun of him for having to work — the very thought of it burnt him like fire. He got out his worldly wealth and examined it — bits of toys, marbles, and trash; enough to buy an exchange of work, maybe, but not half enough to buy so much as half an hour of pure freedom. So he returned his straitened means to his pocket, and gave up the idea of trying to buy the boys. At this dark and hopeless moment an inspiration burst upon him! Nothing less than a great, magnificent inspiration.

He took up his brush and went *tranquilly* to work. Ben Rogers hove in sight presently — the very boy, of all boys, whose *ridicule* he had been dreading. Ben's *gait* was the hop-skip-and-jump — proof enough that his heart was light and his anticipations high. He was eating an apple, and giving a long, melodious whoop, at intervals, followed by a deep-toned ding-dong-dong, ding-dong-dong, for he was *personating* a steamboat. As he drew near, he *slackened* speed, took the middle of the street, leaned far over to *starboard* and rounded to ponderously and with laborious pomp and circumstance — for he was personating the Big Missouri, and considered himself to be drawing nine feet of water. He was boat and captain and engine-bells combined, so he had to imagine himself standing on his own hurricane deck giving the orders and executing them:

"Stop her, sir! Ting-a-ling-ling!" The headway ran almost out and he drew up slowly toward the sidewalk.

"Ship up to back! Ting-a-ling-ling!" His arms straightened and stiffened down his sides.

"Set her back on the starboard! Ting-a-ling-ling! Chow! ch-chow-wow! Chow!" His right hand, meantime, describing stately circles — for it was representing a forty-foot wheel.

"Let her go back on the labboard! Ting-a-ling-ling! Chow-ch-chow-chow!" The left hand began to describe circles.

"Stop the stabboard! Ting-a-ling-ling! Stop the labboard! Come ahead on the stabboard! Stop her! Let your outside turn over slow! Ting-a-ling-ling! Chow-ow-ow! Get out that headline! Lively now! Come — out with your spring-line — what're you about there! Take a turn round that stump with the bight of it! Stand by that stage, now — let her go! Done with the engines, sir! Ting-a-ling-ling! Sh't! sh't! sh't! (trying the gauge cocks).

Tom went on whitewashing — paid no attention to the steamboat. Ben stared a moment and then said:

"Hi-yi. You're up a stump, ain't you!"

No answer. Tom surveyed his last touch with the eye of an artist, then he gave his brush another gentle sweep and surveyed the results, as before. Ben ranged up alongside of him. Tom's mouth watered for the apple, but he stuck to his work. Ben said:

"Hello, old chap, you got to work, hey?"

Tom wheeled suddenly and said:

"Why, it's you, Ben! I warn't noticing."

"Say — I'm going in a-swimming, I am. Don't you wish you could? But of course you'd druther work — wouldn't you? Course you would!"

Tom contemplated the boy a bit, and said:

"What do you call work?"

"Why ain't that work?"

Tom *resumed* his whitewashing, and answered carelessly:

"Well, maybe it is, and maybe it ain't. All I know is, it suits Tom Sawyer."

"Oh come, now, you don't mean to let on that you like it?" The brush continued to move.

"Like it? Well, I don't see why I oughtn't to like it. Does a boy get a chance to whitewash a fence every day?"

That put the thing in a new light. Ben stopped nibbling his apple. Tom swept his brush back and forth — stepped back to note the effect — added a touch here and there — criticized the effect again — Ben watching every move and getting more and more interested, more and more absorbed. Presently he said:

"Say, Tom, let me whitewash a little."

Tom considered, was about to consent; but he *altered* his mind:

"No — no — I reckon it wouldn't hardly do, Ben. You see, Aunt Polly's awful particular about this fence — right here on the street, you know — but if it was the back fence I wouldn't mind and she wouldn't. Yes, she's awful particular about this fence; it's got to be done very careful; I reckon there ain't one boy in a thousand; maybe two thousand, that can do it the way it's got to be done."

"No — is that so? Oh come, now — lemme just try. Only just a little — I'd let you, if you was me, Tom."

"Ben, I'd like to, honest injun; but Aunt Polly — well, Jim wanted to do it, but she wouldn't let him; Sid wanted to do it, but she wouldn't let Sid. Now don't you see how I'm fixed? If you was to tackle this fence and anything was to happen to it —"

"Oh, shucks, I'll be just as careful. Now lemme try. Say — I'll give you the core of my apple."

"Well, here — No, Ben, now don't. I'm afeared —"

"I'll give you all of it!"

Tom gave up the brush with reluctance in his face, but *alacrity* in his heart. And while the late steamer Big Missouri worked and sweated in the sun, the retired artist sat on a barrel in the shade close by, dangled his legs, munched his apple, and planned the slaughter of more innocents. There was no lack of material; boys happened along every little while; they came to *jeer*, but remained to whitewash. By the time Ben was *fagged* out, Tom had traded the next chance to Billy Fisher for a kite, in good repair; and when he played out, Johnny Miller bought in for a dead rat and a string to swing it with — and so on, and so on, hour after hour. And when the middle of the afternoon came, from being a poor poverty-stricken boy in the morning, Tom was literally rolling in wealth. He had, beside the things mentioned, twelve marbles, part of a jew's-harp, a piece of blue bottle-glass to look through, a spool cannon, a key that wouldn't unlock anything, a fragment of chalk, a glass stopper of a decanter, a tin soldier, a couple of tadpoles, six firecrackers, a kitten with only one eye, a brass door-knob, a dog-collar — but no dog — the handle of a knife, four pieces of orange-peel, and a dilapidated old window-sash.

He had a nice, good, idle time all the while — plenty of company — and the fence had three coats of whitewash on it! If he hadn't run out of whitewash, he would have bankrupted every boy in the village.

Tom said to himself that it was not such a hollow world, after all. He had discovered a great law of human action, without knowing it — namely, that in order to make a man or a boy covet a thing, it is only necessary to make the thing difficult to attain. If he had been a great and wise philosopher, like the author of this book, he would now have *comprehended* that Work consists of whatever a body is *obliged* to do, and that Play consists of whatever a body is not obliged to do. And this would help him to understand why constructing artificial flowers or performing on a treadmill is work, while rolling tenpins or climbing Mont Blanc is only amusement. There are wealthy gentlemen in England who drive four-horse passenger coaches twenty or thirty miles on a daily line, in the summer, because the privilege costs them considerable money; but if they were offered wages for the service, that would turn it into work and then they would resign.

The boy *mused* a while over the *substantial* change which had taken place in his worldly circumstances, and then *wended* toward *headquarters* to report.

ABOUT THE AUTHOR

Mark Twain (1835-1920), the pen-name of Samuel Langhorne Clemens, was the foremost American author and humorist of his era. In writing *The Adventures of Tom Sawyer* and its sequel, *The Adventures of Huckleberry Finn,* the author recalls his own boyhood experiences along the Mississippi River. These classic adventures of curious, mischievous, fun-loving boys have become the most widely read boys' stories in American literature.

alacrity — eager readiness
altered — changed
comprehended — understood
delectable — delightful
fagged — tired
gait — manner of walk
headquarters — home
insignificant — small
jeer — mock; laugh
melancholy — sadness
marvel — marble
mused — thought
obliged — forced

personating — acting like; impersonating
ponderously — heavily
retiring — leaving
resumed — continued
ridicule — insults
reposeful — quiet
surveyed — inspected
slackened — slowed
starboard — right side of the ship
substantial — great
tranquilly — calmly
taw — a marble used as a shooter
wended — traveled

BENEATH THE SADDLE

Russell Gordon Carter

Nathan Cathcart, a young pioneer during the
Revolutionary War, found strength and courage
to help his country in a moment of crisis.

Nathan Cathcart sat upright in bed, his heart pounding. In his ears still rang the pistol shot that had awakened him, and from the frozen road at the base of the hill came the clatter of hoof beats. He was about to hurry to the window when a heavy object struck the front door, causing the whole house to tremble.

"Open in the King's name!" came a harsh voice. And another added, "Aye, and be quick!"

Nathan felt his throat tighten. He thought of his mother and longed for her comforting presence, for he was all alone in the little farmhouse. These men at the door were British soldiers; there could be little doubt of that!

With teeth chattering, the boy got hastily into his clothes and made his way down the steep narrow stairway. As he reached the door, it jarred under the powerful blows that threatened to splinter it.

"Who is there?" he called in a shaking voice.

"You will soon find out if you keep us waiting longer!"

Nathan drew aside the heavy oak bar and lifted the latch, and with a rush of cold air the door swung inward. In front of him stood two British soldiers in scarlet uniforms. Beyond them he had a glimpse of others, on their way up the hill, leading their horses.

"Whose house is this?" demanded one

of the men in the doorway. As he spoke, the two of them strode inside.

"I – I live here with my mother," Nathan replied. "Tonight I'm alone, because she had to go to Norfolk to nurse my aunt, who is ill."

"Well, young rebel," the soldier ordered, "go fetch candles, for we mean to have a look about. Mind you lose no time!"

Nathan hesitated, then went into the living room, where squares of moonlight lay upon the wide floor. Why did these men wish to search the house? What could they expect to find?

In a few minutes he was back in the hallway with two lighted candles in brass candlesticks. By that time the rest of the party had reached the house. They strode noisily inside and then closed the door.

"You wait right here, young puppy," one of them said to Nathan.

"But - but what is it you are seeking?" the boy asked.

"Never you mind that," was the reply.

Shivering with cold and excitement, Nathan stood silent beside the door. There were now almost a dozen soldiers in the house, some of them upstairs, some on the lower floor. The candles, which they carried from room to room, sent queer shadows dancing wildly about on walls and floor and ceiling. From snatches of conversation, Nathan understood that they were searching for someone, but he could not find out who it might be.

At least those on the second floor came clumping down the stairs. "We are wasting our time here!" one of them shouted. Then the whole party went outside. Standing in the doorway, Nathan saw them mount their horses and ride down the hillside toward the road.

Closing the door, he went upstairs. There he found the bedrooms in great disorder. On the floor of his own room a candle was burning dangerously close to the bed covering. He carried it downstairs and placed it upon the high mantelpiece above the fireplace, where the soldiers had left the second one. Despite the cold that filled the room, he stood for some time motionless before the hearth, his head bent, his forehead wrinkled. Who was it the British soldiers were seeking? He remembered the pistol that had awakened him. What did it all mean?

Outside the wind was rising. He heard the mournful sound of it in the chimney and among the pines that sheltered the house on the northwest. Now and then a beam would crack with the cold. The boy hunched his shoulders and thought of his bed with its warm blankets.

Stepping forward, he snuffed out the candles. He was on his way toward the stairs when a gentle knock at the door caused him to stiffen and catch his breath. His first thought was that the soldiers had returned. "But no redcoat would knock like that!" he thought to himself. He went close to the door. "Who is there?" he asked.

"A friend," came the reply in a low voice.

Nathan hesitated. "Who are you?" he demanded.

"A friend," the voice repeated.

Nathan swung the door open and then uttered a little cry of surprise. There in the moonlight stood a man in the uniform of the American army, a bloodstained kerchief

The man lifted his head. "Lad," he said, "I have made a sorry mess of an important errand. My name is Dawson, and I was carrying important papers from General Washington, at White Plains. The British laid an ambush for me. I tried to escape them by desperate riding, but they fired, and a pistol ball grazed the side of my head, causing me to lose control of my horse. The creature raced up the road and then bolted into the woods, where a branch swept me to the ground. They found my horse, but they were unable to find me!"

"Oh," exclaimed Nathan, "then 'tis not so bad after all!"

"Not so bad?" repeated the messenger. "In truth, affairs could hardly be worse!"

Nathan looked at him wonderingly.

"The papers I carried were on the horse," Dawson added bitterly. "I had thrust the packet 'twixt saddle and blanket, thinking it would be safe, and now the British have my horse! They will soon discover the packet, if they have not already come upon it, and then - - " He flung out his hands in despair. "Ah, if only - - "

He suddenly checked himself and rose to his feet. From the direction of the road came the ring and clatter of hoof beats and the sound of excited voices. The British soldiers were returning!

"Come!" cried Nathan, seizing the man's arm. "You must hide!"

"Aye, but where?" Dawson glanced wildly about.

Nathan strode to the great fireplace and stepped inside. With shoulder against the wooden wall at one end, he pressed until it yielded, revealing an opening perhaps a foot wide. "Squeeze in there!" he ordered. "Then push the wall back into place. My grandfather once hid there from the Indians. You will be safe if you make no sound. Quick!" He pushed the man forward.

Only when the panel had closed behind the stranger was Nathan able to control his trembling hands. Running to the window, he beheld the whole troop riding at a fast pace up the hillside. What should he do? Suddenly he ran to the door, slid back the bar which had held it fast, and then went

round his head. In a flash the boy understood. This was the man for whom the British were searching!

"Thank ye, lad," said the stranger as he entered the house. "The night is cold — — "

"And they've wounded you!"

"Aye, that is true, but 'tis not a bad wound." The man laughed bitterly. "So they thought to find me in the house, eh? Little they knew that I was watching while they came up the hill! You are alone here, lad?"

"Yes," said Nathan. "My mother is at Norfolk for a day or two."

In the living room the stranger dropped wearily upon a bench in front of the hearth and covered his face with his hands. "A sorry mess I have made of things!" he muttered.

Nathan listened uneasily. "What has happened, sir?" he said. "I — I would like to be of help, if there is anything that I can do!"

swiftly up the stairway to his room. He flung himself into his cold bed.

A few seconds later he heard the soldiers in the hall, then in the lower rooms. He lay with thumping heart while the stairs *resounded* under the tread of heavy boots. Now the redcoats were on the second floor. Now they were in his room! One of them held up a candle, revealing the boy sitting up, wide-eyed, in bed, the blankets about his shoulders.

"Where is the rebel horseman? Where is he hiding?"

Nathan swallowed hard and remained silent.

"Speak up, young whelp!"

Before the boy could answer, a soldier caught hold of him and flung him onto the floor. Then they began to prod the mattress with the points of their swords.

Bruised and shaken, Nathan rose and made his way downstairs, intending to flee to the nearby woods. As he stepped from the doorway, he almost ran into a soldier who was holding the bridles of half a dozen horses.

"Wait a bit, lad!" the man exclaimed, and his voice sounded kind. "Wait a bit, I say. We mean ye no harm, and that is the truth!"

Nathan hesitated.

"'Tis a cold night!" said the soldier, blowing on his hands. "The horses feel it, too!"

Steam from their nostrils rose white and sparkling in the moonlight. The frozen earth rang under their restlessly stamping feet.

"They are fine-looking horses, sir," Nathan remarked with an effort.

"Aye, fine animals indeed!"

The boy was studying them carefully. Which was the dispatch rider's horse? He singled out a sleek black mare that looked more tired than the others. And then he noticed that her saddle was different from the other saddles!

In a friendly, careless manner, he walked over to her and patted her nose. At that moment one of the soldiers stepped to the doorway and began to talk to the man who held the bridles. Nathan heard no word of what they were saying, for his fingers were

upon the mare's blanket, creeping upward under the saddle, while the terrific beating of his heart seemed to jar his whole body! At last his fingers touched something. . . something. . .Just then one of the British horses nipped at the black mare, and she backed away, almost knocking the boy over.

"Steady, there!" yelled the redcoat, and then he continued his talk with the man in the doorway.

As Nathan thrust his fingers under the saddle again, he heard the soldiers coming down the stairs. Evidently the search was ended, and they were about to ride off! Again his hand was touching something beneath the saddle. With thumb and forefinger upon a corner of the object, he drew it slowly downward. The moonlight flashed for an instant on an oblong white packet as he jerked it forth and thrust it beneath his shirt.

Nathan was nowhere in sight when the British rode off. He had run to the shelter of a brush heap at the north of the house, ready to retreat further into the woods if the soldiers should decide to hunt for him. But they were not interested in a mere boy. They had searched the house twice and were satisfied that the rebel horseman was not within.

The British had been gone at least a quarter of an hour when Nathan entered the living room and thrust his shoulder against the panel at the end of the fireplace. Dawson stepped forth, blinking in the candlelight. "Eh, what -- what -- ?"

"I took it from beneath the saddle," said Nathan.

"You -- you -- what?" With a hoarse cry the man seized the packet and examined it. Then his legs wavered under him, and he sat down hard upon the bench. "Lad!" he muttered. "You -- you tricked them!" Suddenly he sprang to his feet and threw his arms about Nathan's shoulders. "You've done me a service! Aye, you've done your country a service! I'll never forget it as long as I live! Tell me your name, lad!"

"Nathan Cathcart, sir."

"Cathcart, eh? I'll not be likely to forget that name! I had a friend, Jack Cathcart,

resounded — echoed

who fell at Bunker Hill."

"He was my father," Nathan said in a low voice. For several seconds the man and boy stood facing each other in silence. . .

"Well, lad," the soldier said at last, "I must be off. The Blue Fox Tavern lies but a few miles up the road, and there I can get another horse. Your hand, Nathan, and I promise you that General Washington shall hear of what has happened this night!"

Nathan watched him as he made his way down the slope in the moonlight. Then the boy climbed the stairs once more to his room, this time to undisturbed sleep!

THINKING IT THROUGH

1. How did Nathan Cathcart find the horse that carried the papers?
2. Under the very nose of the enemy, Nathan Cathcart seized the opportunity to help his country. What opportunities do you have to serve America today?
3. Write an essay telling about a project you will carry out to serve your country.

WHAT I LIVE FOR

— George Linnaeus Banks

I live for those who love me,
  Whose hearts are kind and true,
For the heaven that smiles above me,
  And awaits my spirit too;
For all human ties that bind me,
For the task by God assigned me,
For the bright hopes left behind me,
  And the good that I can do.

I live to learn their story
  Who suffered for my sake;
To *emulate* their glory
  And follow in their wake:
Bards, patriots, martyrs, sages
The heroic of all ages,
Whose deeds crown history's pages,
  And time's great volume make.

I live to hold communion
  With all that is divine;
To feel there is a union
  'Twixt Nature's heart and mine;
To profit by *affliction*,
Reap truths from fields of fiction,
Grow wiser from *conviction*,
  And fulfill God's grand design.

I live for those who love me,
  For those who know me true;
For the heaven that smiles above me,
  And awaits my spirit too;
For the cause that lacks assistance,
For the wrong that needs resistance,
For the future in the distance,
  And the good that I can do.

emulate — strive to equal
Bards — poets of heroic verse
affliction — suffering; trials
conviction — strong belief

THE GREAT STONE FACE

Nathaniel Hawthorne

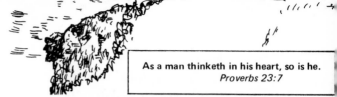

> As a man thinketh in his heart, so is he.
> *Proverbs 23:7*

Thoughts are building-blocks of character. Someone has said if you'll tell me what you think about, I'll tell you what you are. Does this seem unreasonable? It is true in principle, for what we think is ultimately what we become. Hawthorne weaves this truth into his legend of the Great Stone Face, a story based on a human-like rock formation in the White Mountains of New Hampshire called "The Old Man of the Mountain."

One afternoon, when the sun was going down, a mother and her little boy sat at the door of their cottage, talking about the Great Stone Face. They had only to lift their eyes, and there it could be plainly seen, though miles away, with the sunshine brightening all its features.

And what was the Great Stone Face?

Cradled among a family of lofty mountains, there was a valley so spacious that it contained many thousand inhabitants. Some of these good people dwelt in log-huts on the steep and difficult hillsides with the black forest all around them. Others lived in comfortable farmhouses, and cultivated the rich soil on the gentle slopes or level surfaces of the valley. Still others congregated into populous villages, where some wild, highland brook, tumbling down from its birthplace in the upper mountain region, had been caught and tamed by human skill, and forced to turn the machinery of cotton factories. The inhabitants of this valley, in short, were numerous and of many modes of life. But all of them, grown people and children, were familiar with the Great Stone Face, although some possessed the gift of distinguishing this grand natural phenomenon more perfectly than many of their neighbors.

The Great Stone Face, then, was a work of Nature in her mood of majestic playfulness, formed on the steep side of a mountain by some huge rocks which had been thrown together in such a position as to resemble the features of the human countenance when viewed at a proper distance. It seemed as if an enormous giant, or a *Titan*, had sculptured his own likeness on the precipice. There was the broad arch of the forehead, a hundred feet in height; the nose, with its long bridge; and the vast lips, which, if they could have spoken, would have rolled their thunder accents from one end of the valley to the other. It is true, that if the spectator approached too near, he lost the outline of the gigantic face, and could see only a heap of heavy, gigantic rocks piled in *chaotic* ruin one upon another. Retracing his steps, however, the wondrous features would again be seen; and the farther he withdrew from them, the more like a human face, with all its original divinity intact, did they appear; until, as it grew dim in the distance, with the clouds and glorified mist of the mountains clustering about it, the Great Stone Face seemed positively to be alive.

It was a happy lot for children to grow up to manhood or womanhood with the Great Stone Face before their eyes, for all the features were noble, and the expression was at once grand and sweet, as if it were the glow of a vast, warm heart that embraced all mankind in its affections, and had room for more. It was an education only to look at it. According to the belief of many people, the valley owed much of its fertility to this kind countenance.

As we began saying, a mother and her little boy sat at their cottage door gazing at the Great Stone Face and talking about it. The child's name was Ernest.

"Mother," he said, while the Titanic face smiled on him, "I wish that it could speak, for it looks so very kind that its voice must be pleasant. If I were to see a man with such a face, I should love him dearly."

"If an old prophecy comes to pass," answered his mother, "we may see a man, some time or other, with exactly such a face as that."

"What *prophecy* do you mean, dear mother?" eagerly inquired Ernest. "Pray tell me all about it!"

So his mother told him a story that her own mother had told to her, when she herself was younger than little Ernest; a story of what was yet to come; a story, nevertheless, so very old that even the Indians, who formerly inhabited this valley, had heard it from their forefathers, to whom they declared it had been murmured by the mountain streams, and whispered by the wind among the tree-tops. The meaning was that at some future day, a child should be born nearby who was destined to become the greatest and noblest person of his time, and whose countenance in manhood should bear an exact resemblance to the Great Stone Face. Many old-fashioned people and young ones alike, in the ardor of their hopes, still cherished an enduring faith in this old prophecy. But others, who had seen more of the world, had watched and waited till they were weary, and had beheld no man with such a face, nor any man that proved to be much greater or nobler than his neighbors; these people concluded it to be nothing but an idle tale. At all events, the great man of the prophecy had not yet appeared.

"O mother, dear mother!" cried Ernest, clapping his hands above his head. "I do hope that I shall live to see him!"

His mother was an affectionate and thoughtful woman, and felt that it was wisest not to discourage the generous hopes of her little boy. So she only said to him, "Perhaps you may."

And Ernest never forgot the story that his mother told him. It was always in his mind when he looked upon the Great Stone Face. He spent his childhood in the log-cottage where he was born, and was dutiful to his mother, and helpful to her in many things, assisting her much with his little hands, and more with his loving heart. In this manner, from a happy yet often *pensive* child, he grew up to be a mild, quiet, unnoticed boy, sun-browned with labor in the fields, but with more intelligence brightening his face than is seen in many lads who have been taught at famous schools. Yet Ernest had had no teacher, except that the Great Stone Face became one to him. When the toil of the day was over, he would gaze at it for hours, until he began to imagine that those vast features recognized him and gave him a smile of kindness and encouragement in response to his own look of respect. We must not take upon us to affirm that this was a mistake, although the Face may have looked no more kindly at Ernest than at all the world besides. But the secret was that other people could not see; and thus the love, which was meant for all, became his special portion.

About this time there went a rumor throughout the valley that the great man, foretold from ages long ago, who was to bear a resemblance to the Great Stone Face, had appeared at last. It seems that many years before, a young man had left the valley and settled at a distant seaport where, after getting together a little money, he had become a shopkeeper. His name-- but I could never learn whether it was his real one, or a nickname that had grown out of his habits and success in life--was Gathergold. Being shrewd and active, and endowed by Providence with that inscrutable faculty which the world calls luck, he became an exceedingly rich merchant, and owner of a whole fleet of bulky-bottomed ships. All the countries of the globe appeared to join hands for the mere purpose of adding heap after heap to the mountainous accumulation of this one man's wealth. The cold regions of the north, almost within the gloom and shadow of the Arctic Circle, sent him their tribute in furs; hot Africa sifted for him the golden sands of her rivers, and gathered up the ivory tusks of her great elephants out of the forests; the East came bringing him the rich shawls, and spices, and teas, and the brilliance of diamonds, and the gleaming purity of large pearls. The ocean, not to be behind the earth, yielded up her mighty whales that Mr. Gathergold might sell their oil, and make a profit on it. Be the first item what it might, it became gold within his grasp. It might be said of him, as of Midas in the fable, that whatever he touched with his finger immediately glistened, and grew yellow, and was changed at once into sterling metal, or, which suited him still better, into piles of gold coins. And when Mr. Gathergold had become so very rich that it would have taken him a hundred years only to count his wealth, he remembered his native valley, and resolved to go back there and end his days where he was born. With this purpose in view, he sent a skilled architect to build him a palace fit for a man of his vast wealth to live in.

As I have said above, it had already been rumored in the valley that Mr. Gathergold had turned out to be the prophetic person so long and vainly looked for, and that his face was the perfect and undeniable likeness of the Great Stone Face. People were even more ready to believe that this must be true when they saw the splendid building that rose as if by magic on the site of his father's old weatherbeaten farmhouse. The *exterior* was of marble so dazzlingly white that it seemed as though the whole structure might melt away in the sunshine, like those humbler ones which Mr. Gathergold, in his young play-days, had been accustomed to build of snow. It had a richly ornamented entrance, supported by tall pillars, beneath which was a high door studded with silver knobs and made of a kind of variegated wood that had been brought from beyond the sea. The windows, from the floor to the ceiling of each stately apartment, were made of one enormous pane of glass so transparent that it was said to be a clearer medium than even the vacant atmosphere.

Hardly anybody had been permitted to see the *interior* of this palace; but it was reported, and with good semblance of truth, to be far more gorgeous than the outside insomuch that whatever was iron or brass in other houses was silver or gold in this; and Mr. Gathergold's bedchamber, especially, made such a glittering appearance that no ordinary man would have been able to close his eyes there. But on the other hand, Mr. Gathergold was now so accustomed to wealth that perhaps he could not have closed his eyes unless the gleam of it was certain to find its way beneath his eyelids.

In due time the mansion was finished; next came the upholsterers, with magnificent furniture; then, a whole troop of black and white servants. Mr. Gathergold, in his own majestic person, was expected to arrive at sunset. Our friend Ernest, meanwhile, had been deeply stirred by the idea that the great man, the noble man, the man of prophecy, after so many ages of delay, was at length to be made known to his native valley. He knew, boy as he was, that there were a thousand ways in which Mr. Gathergold, with his vast wealth, might become an angel of kindness and assume a control over human affairs as wide and gracious as the smile of the Great Stone Face. Full of faith and hope, Ernest believed that what the people said was true, and that now he was to behold the living likeness of those wondrous features on the mountainside. While the boy was still gazing up the valley and fancying, as he always did, that the Great Stone Face returned his gaze and looked kindly at him, the rumbling of wheels was heard approaching swiftly along the winding road.

"Here he comes!" cried a group of people who were assembled to witness the arrival. "Here comes the great Mr. Gathergold!"

A carriage drawn by four horses dashed around the turn of the road. Within it, thrust partly out of the window, appeared the face of the old man, with a skin as yellow as if his own Midas-hand had changed it. He had a low forehead, small sharp eyes puckered about with innumerable wrinkles, and very thin lips which he made still thinner by forcing them together.

"The very image of the Great Stone Face!" shouted the people. "Sure enough, the old prophecy is true; and here we have the great man at last!"

And what greatly puzzled Ernest, they seemed actually to believe that here was the likeness which they spoke of. By the roadside there happened to be an old beggar-woman and two little beggar-children, stragglers from some far-off region, who, as the carriage rolled onward, held out their hands and lifted up their sad voices, most piteously beseeching charity. A yellow hand--the very same that had clawed together so much wealth--poked itself out of the coach-window, and dropped some copper coins upon the ground; so that, though the great man's name seems to have been Gathergold, he might just as suitably have been nicknamed Scattercopper. Nevertheless, with an earnest shout, and with as much good faith as ever, the people shouted--

"He is the very image of the Great Stone Face!"

But Ernest turned sadly from the wrinkled hardness of that greedy face, and gazed up at the valley where, amid a gathering mist and gilded by the last sunbeams, he could still see those glorious features which had impressed themselves into his soul. Their aspect cheered him. What did the kind lip seem to say?

"He will come! Fear not, Ernest; the man will come!"

The years went on, and Ernest was no longer a boy. He had grown to be a young man now. He attracted little notice from the other inhabitants of the valley, for they saw nothing unusual in his way of life except that when the labor of the day was over, he still loved to go apart and gaze and meditate upon the Great Stone Face. According to their idea of the matter, it was foolish indeed, but pardonable because Ernest was industrious, kind, and neighborly, and did not neglect duty for the sake of indulging this idle habit. They did not know that the Great Stone Face had become a teacher to him, and that the sentiment which was expressed in it would enlarge the young man's heart and fill it with wider and deeper sympathies than other hearts. They did not know that from this would come a better wisdom than could be learned from books, and a better life than could be molded on the marred example of other human lives. Neither did Ernest know that the thoughts and affections which came to him so naturally in the fields and at the fireside and wherever he communed with himself were of a higher tone than those which all men shared with him. A simple soul--simple as when his mother first taught him the old prophecy-- he beheld the marvelous features beaming down the valley and still wondered why their human counterpart was so long in making his appearance.

By this time poor Mr. Gathergold was

dead and buried; and the oddest part of the matter was that his wealth, which was the body and spirit of his existence, had disappeared before his death, leaving nothing of him but a living skeleton covered over with a wrinkled, yellow skin. Since the melting away of his gold, it had been very generally admitted that there was no such striking resemblance, after all, between the snobbish features of the ruined merchant and that majestic face upon the mountainside. So the people ceased to honor him during his life time, and quietly forgot him after his death. Once in a while, it is true, his memory was brought up in connection with the magnificent palace which he had built, and which had long ago been turned into a hotel to accommodate the multitude of strangers who came every summer to visit that famous natural curiosity, the Great Stone Face. Thus, Mr. Gathergold being discredited, the man of prophecy was yet to come.

It so happened that a native-born son of the valley had enlisted as a soldier many years before, and, after a great deal of hard fighting, had now become an outstanding commander. Whatever he may be called in history, he was known in camps and on the battlefield under the nickname of Old Blood-and-Thunder. This war-worn veteran, now infirm with age and wounds, and weary of the turmoil of military life, of the roll of the drum and the noise of the trumpet that had so long been ringing in his ears, had lately indicated that he would return to his native valley, hoping to find rest where he remembered to have left it. His old neighbors and their grown-up children decided to welcome the famous warrior with a salute of cannon and a public dinner; they worked even more enthusiastically because they now believed that at last, the likeness of the Great Stone Face had actually appeared. An aid-de-camp of Old Blood-and-Thunder, traveling through the valley, was said to have been struck with the resemblance. Moreover the schoolmates and early acquaintances of the general were ready to testify on oath that to the best of their recollection, the general had been exceedingly like the majestic

image even when a boy, only that the idea had never occurred to them at that time. Great was the excitement throughout the valley; and many people who had not once thought of glancing at the Great Stone Face for years, now spent their time gazing at it for the sake of knowing exactly how General Blood-and-Thunder looked.

On the day of the great festival, Ernest and all the other people of the valley left their work and proceeded to the spot where the banquet was prepared. As he approached, the loud voice of the Rev. Dr. Battleblast was heard beseeching a blessing on the good things set before them and on the distinguished friend of peace in whose honor they were assembled. The tables were arranged in a cleared space of the woods, shut in by the surrounding trees except where an eastward opening afforded a distant view of the Great Stone Face. Over the general's chair, which was an antique from the home of Washington, there was an arch of green boughs abundantly intermingled with laurel and surmounted by his country's banner, beneath which he had won his victories. Our friend Ernest raised himself on his tiptoes hoping to get a glimpse of the celebrated guest; but there was a mighty crowd about the tables anxious to hear the toasts and speeches and to catch any word that might fall from the general in reply; and a volunteer company, acting as a guard, pricked ruthlessly with their bayonets at any particularly quiet person among the throng. So Ernest, being of a quiet character, was thrust quite into the background where he could see no more of Old Blood-and-Thunder's face than if it had been still blazing on the battlefield. To comfort himself, he turned toward the Great Stone Face, which, like a faithful and long-remembered friend, looked back and smiled upon him through the *vista* of the forest. Meanwhile, however, he could overhear the remarks of various individuals who were comparing the features of the hero with the face on the distant mountain-side.

" 'Tis the same face, to a hair!" cried one man, jumping for joy.

"Wonderfully alike, that's a fact!"

responded another.

"Alike! Why, call it Old Blood-and-Thunder himself, in a huge looking glass!" cried a third. "And why not? He's the greatest man of this or any other age, beyond a doubt."

And then all three of the speakers gave a great shout which stirred up the crowd and called forth a roar from a thousand voices that went echoing for miles among the mountains until you might have supposed that the Great Stone Face had poured its thunder-breath into the cry. All these comments and this vast enthusiasm served the more to interest our friend; nor did he think of questioning that now, at last, the mountain-visage had found its human counter-part. It is true, Ernest had imagined that this long-looked-for person would appear in the character of a man of peace, uttering wisdom, and doing good, and making people happy. But, taking a habitual broad view, with all his simplicity, he contended that *Providence* should choose its own method of blessing mankind, and he could believe that this great end might be effected even by a warrior and a bloody sword, if divine Wisdom chose to order matters so.

"The general! the general!" was now the cry. "Hush! Silence! Old Blood-and-Thunder's going to make a speech."

Even so, for when the cloth had been removed and the general's health had been drunk amid shouts of applause, he stood upon his feet to thank the company. Ernest saw him. There he was, over the shoulders of the crowd, from the two glittering *epaulets* and embroidered collar upward, beneath the arch of green boughs with intertwined laurel, and the banner drooping as if to shade his brow! And there, too, visible in the same glance, through the opening of the forest, appeared the Great Stone Face! And was there, indeed, such a resemblance as the crowd had testified? Alas, Ernest could not recognize it! He beheld a war-worn and weatherbeaten countenance, full of energy, and expressive of iron will; but the gentle wisdom, the deep, broad, tender sympathies, were altogether missing in Old Blood-and-

Thunder's face; and even if the Great Stone Face had assumed his look of stern command, milder traits would still have softened it.

"This is not the man of prophecy," sighed Ernest to himself, as he made his way out of the throng. "And must the world wait longer yet?"

The mists had gathered about the distant mountain-side, and there were seen the grand and awesome features of the Great Stone Face, awesome but kind, as if a mighty angel were sitting among the hills and enrobing himself in a cloud-garment of gold and purple. As he looked, Ernest believed that a smile beamed over the whole face, with a brightening radiance, although without motion of the lips. It was probably the effect of the western sunshine melting through the thinly scattered mist that had swept between him and the object that he gazed at. But, as it always did, the aspect of his marvelous friend made Ernest as hopeful as if he had never hoped in vain.

"Fear not, Ernest," said his heart, even as if the Great Stone Face were whispering to him—"fear not, Ernest; he will come."

More years sped swiftly and quietly away. Ernest still dwelt in his native valley and was now a man of middle age. By gradual degrees he had become known among the people. Now, as before, he labored for his bread and was the same simple-hearted man that he had always been. But he had thought and felt so much, he had given so many of the best hours of his life to unworldly hopes for some great good to mankind, that it seemed as though he had been talking with the angels and had received a portion of their wisdom unawares. It was visible in the calm and well-considered kindness of his daily life, the quiet stream of which had made a wide green margin all along its course. Not a day passed by that the world was not the better because this man, humble as he was, had lived. He never stepped aside from his own path, yet would always bring a blessing to his neighbor. Almost involuntarily, too, he had become a preacher. The pure, high simplicity of his thought took shape in the good deeds that dropped silently from his hand and flowed forth in speech. He uttered truths that worked upon and molded the lives of those who heard him. His hearers never suspected that Ernest, their own neighbor and familiar friend, was more than an ordinary man; least of all did Ernest himself suspect it; but, sure as the murmur of a brook, came thoughts out of his mouth that no other human lips had spoken.

When the people's minds had had a little time to cool, they were ready enough to acknowledge their mistake in imagining a similarity between General Blood-and-Thunder's harsh face and the kind countenance on the mountain-side. But now again there were reports, and many paragraphs in the newspapers, affirming that the likeness of the Great Stone Face had appeared upon the broad shoulders of a certain famous statesman. He, like Mr. Gathergold and Old Blood-and-Thunder, was a native of the valley, but had left it in his early days, and taken up the trades of law and politics.

Instead of the rich man's wealth and the warrior's sword, he had but a tongue, and it was mightier than both together. So wonderfully eloquent was he, that whatever he might choose to say, his listeners had no choice but to believe him; wrong looked like right, and right like wrong; for when it pleased him, he could make a kind of intellectual fog with his mere breath, and hide the truth with it. His tongue, indeed, was a magic instrument: sometimes it rumbled like the thunder; sometimes it warbled like the sweetest music. It was the blast of war, the song of peace; and it seemed to have a heart in it, when there was no such matter. In good truth, he was a wondrous man; and when his tongue had acquired him all other imaginable success, when it had been heard in halls of state, and in the courts of princes and rulers, after it had made him known all over the world, even as a voice crying from shore to shore, it finally persuaded his countrymen to select him for the Presidency. Before this time--indeed, as soon as he began to grow famous--his admirers had found the resemblance between him and the Great Stone Face and so much were they struck by it that throughout the country this distinguished gentlemen was known by the name of Old Stony Phiz.

While his friends were doing their best to make him President, Old Stony Phiz, as he was called, set out on a visit to the valley where he was born. Of course, he had no other object than to shake hands with his fellow-citizens, and neither thought nor cared about any effect which his progress through the country might have upon the election. Magnificent preparations were made to receive the illustrious statesman; a *cavalcade* of horsemen set forth to meet him at the boundary line of the state, and all the people left their business and gathered along the wayside to see him pass. Among these was Ernest. Though more than once disappointed, as we have seen, he had such a hopeful and trusting nature that he was always ready to believe in whatever seemed beautiful and good. He kept his heart continually open, and thus was sure to catch the blessing from on high when it should come. So now again, as *buoyantly* as ever, he went forth to behold the likeness of the Great Stone Face.

The cavalcade came prancing along the road, with a great clattering of hoofs and a mighty cloud of dust, which rose up so thick and high that the visage of the mountainside was completely hidden from Ernest's eyes. All the great men of the neighborhood were there on horseback; militia officers, in uniform; the member of Congress; the sheriff of the county; the editors of newspapers. Many a farmer, too, with his Sunday coat upon his back, had mounted his patient *steed.* It really was a very brilliant spectacle, especially as there were numerous banners flying over the cavalcade on which were gorgeous portraits of the illustrious statesman and the Great Stone Face, smiling familiarly at one another like two brothers. If the pictures were to be trusted, the mutual resemblance, it must be confessed, was marvelous. We must not forget to mention that there was a band of music which made the echoes of the mountains ring and echo with the loud triumph of its strains, so that airy and soul-thrilling melodies broke out among all the heights and hollows as if every nook of his native valley had found a voice to welcome the distinguished guest. But the grandest effect was when the far-off mountain flung back the music; for then the Great Stone Face itself seemed to be swelling the triumphant chorus, declaring that at length the man of prophecy was come.

All this while the people were throwing up their hats and shouting with enthusiasm so contagious that the heart of Ernest kindled up, and he likewise threw up his hat and shouted as loudly as the loudest, "Hurray for the great man! Hurray for Old Stony Phiz!" But as yet he had not seen him.

"Here he is, now!" cried those who stood near Ernest. "There! There! Look at Old Stony Phiz and then at the Old Man of the Mountain, and see if they are not as like as twin brothers!"

In the midst of all this gallant array came an open carriage drawn by four white horses; and in the carriage, with his large head uncovered, sat the *illustrious* statesman, Old Stony Phiz himself.

"Confess it," said one of Ernest's neighbors to him, "The Great Stone Face has met his match at last!"

Now it must be owned that at his first glimpse of the countenance which was bowing and smiling from the *barouche,* Ernest did fancy that there was a resemblance between it and the old familiar face upon the mountain-side. The brow, with its massive depth and loftiness, and all the other features were boldly and strongly formed, as if in imitation of a more than heroic model. But the nobility and stateliness, the grand expression of a divine sympathy that enlightened the mountain visage and changed its heavy granite substance into spirit, could not be found here. Something had been originally left out, or had departed. And therefore the marvelously gifted statesman always had a weary gloom in the depths of his eyes, like a child that has outgrown its playthings or a man of great abilities and small aims, whose life, with all its high accomplishments, was meaningless and empty because no high purpose had enriched it with reality.

Still, Ernest's neighbor was thrusting his elbow into his side, and pressing him for an answer.

"Confess! confess! Is not he the very picture of your Old Man of the Mountain?"

"No!" said Ernest, bluntly, "I see little or no likeness."

"Then so much the worse for the Great Stone Face!" answered his neighbor-and again he set up a shout for Old Stony Phiz.

But Ernest turned away, sad, and almost discouraged; for this was the saddest of his disappointments, to behold a man who might have fulfilled the prophecy, and had not willed to do so. Meantime, the cavalcade, the banners, the music, and the carriages swept past him with the noisy crowd in the rear, leaving the dust to settle down, and the Great Stone Face to be revealed with the grandeur that it had worn for centuries.

"Lo, here I am, Ernest!" the kind lips seemed to say. "I have waited longer than you, and am not yet weary. Fear not; the man will come."

The years hurried onward, treading in their haste on one another's heels. And now they began to bring white hairs, and scatter them over Ernest's head; they made reverend wrinkles across his forehead, and furrows in his cheeks. He was an aged man. But he had not grown old in vain: more than the white hairs on his head were the wise thoughts in his mind; his wrinkles and furrows were inscriptions that Time had engraved, and in which he had written legends of wisdom that had been tested by the course of a life. And Ernest had stopped being unknown. Unsought for, undesired, had come the fame which so many seek, and made him known in the great world beyond the limits of the valley in which he had dwelt so quietly. College professors, and even the active men of cities, came from far to see and speak with Ernest; for the report had gone abroad that this simple farmer had ideas unlike those of other men--not gained from books, but of a higher tone--a quiet and informal majesty, as if he had been talking with the angels as his daily freinds. Whether it were *sage,* statesman, or *philanthropist,* Ernest received these visitors with the gentle sincerity that had characterized him from boyhood, and spoke freely with them of whatever came first, or lay deepest in his heart or their own. While they talked together, his face would kindle, unawares, and shine upon them as with a mild evening light. Thoughtful after speaking with him, his guests took leave and went their way, and as they passed up the valley they paused to look at the Great Stone Face, imagining that they had seen its likeness in a human face, but could not remember where.

While Ernest had been growing up and growing old, a bountiful Providence had granted a new poet to this earth. He, likewise, was a native of the valley, but had spent the greater part of his life at a distance from that romantic region, pouring out his sweet music amid the bustle and din of cities. Often, however, the mountains, which had been familiar to him in his childhood, lifted their snowy peaks into the clear atmosphere of his poetry. Neither was the Great Stone Face forgotten, for the poet had written about it in a lyric poem which was grand enough to have been uttered by its own majestic lips. This man of genius, we may say, had come down from heaven with wonderful endowments. If he sang of a mountain, the eyes of all mankind beheld a mightier grandeur resting on its breast, or soaring to its peak, than had been seen there before. If his theme were a lovely lake, a heavenly smile had now been thrown over it to gleam forever on its surface. If it were the vast old sea,

even the deep immensity of its dread bosom seemed to swell the higher, as if moved by the emotions of the song. Thus the world assumed another and a better aspect from the hour that the poet blessed it with his happy eyes. The Creator had bestowed him as the last, best touch to his own handiwork. Creation was not finished till the poet came to interpret, and so complete it.

The effect was no less high and beautiful when people were the subject of his verse. The man or woman, clothed with the common dust of life, who crossed his daily path, and the little child who played in it, were glorified if he beheld them in his mood of poetic faith. He showed the golden links of the great chain that intertwined them with an angelic kindred; he brought out the hidden traits of a *celestial* birth that made them worthy of such kin. Some thought to show the soundness of their judgment by declaring that all the beauty and dignity of the natural world existed only in the poet's imagination. Let such men speak for themselves, who undoubtedly seem to have been brought forth by Nature with a contemptuous bitterness; she had formed them out of her refuse stuff after all the swine were made. As respects all other things, the poet's ideal was the truest truth.

The songs of this poet found their way to Ernest. He read them after his customary toil, seated on the bench before his cottage door, where for such a length of time he had filled his rest with thought by gazing at the Great Stone Face. And now as he read stanzas that caused his soul to thrill within him, he lifted his eyes to the vast countenance beaming on him so kindly.

"O majestic friend," he murmured, addressing the Great Stone Face, "is not this man worthy to resemble thee?"

The face seemed to smile, but answered not a word.

Now it happened that the poet, though he dwelt so far away, had not only heard of Ernest, but had thought much upon his character until nothing seemed so desirable as to meet this man whose untaught wisdom walked hand in hand with the noble simplicity of his life. One summer morning, therefore, he took passage by the railroad, and in the late afternoon alighted from the train not far from Ernest's cottage. The great hotel, which had formerly been the palace of Mr. Gathergold, was close at hand, but the poet, with his carpet-bag on his arm, inquired at once where Ernest dwelt, and was resolved to be accepted as his guest.

Approaching the door, he found the good old man holding a volume in his hand, which alternately he read, and then, with a finger between the leaves, looked lovingly at the Great Stone Face.

"Good evening," said the poet. "Can you give a traveler a night's lodging?"

"Willingly," answered Ernest; and then he added, smiling, "I think I have never seen the Great Stone Face look so hospitably at a stranger."

The poet sat down on the bench beside him, and he and Ernest talked together. Often the poet had talked with the wittiest and the wisest but never before with a man like Ernest, whose thoughts and feelings gushed up with such a natural freedom, and who made great truths so familiar by his simple utterance of them. Angels, as had been so often said, seemed to have worked with him at his labor in the fields; angels seemed to have sat with him by the fireside; and, dwelling with angels as friend with friends, he had combined their exalted ideas with the sweet and lowly charm of simple words. So thought the poet. Ernest, on the other hand, was moved and excited by the living images which the poet flung out of his mind, images which seemed to fill all the air about the cottage door with shapes of beauty both gay and thoughtful. The sympathies of these two men taught them with a greater sense of completeness than either could have attained alone. Their minds accorded into one strain, and made delightful music which neither of them could have claimed as all his own, nor distinguished his own share from the other's. They led one another, as it were, into a high pavilion of thought so distant and until now so dim, that they had never

entered it before, and so beautiful that they desired to be there always.

As Ernest listened to the poet, he imagined that the Great Stone Face was bending forward to listen, too. He gazed earnestly into the poet's glowing eyes.

"Who are you, my strangely gifted guest?" he said.

The poet laid his finger on the volume that Ernest had been reading.

"You have read these poems," said he. "You know me, then, for I wrote them."

Again, and still more earnestly than before, Ernest examined the poet's features; then turned toward the Great Stone Face; then back, with an uncertain expression, to his guest. But his countenance fell; he shook his head, and sighed.

"Why are you sad?" inquired the poet.

"Because," replied Ernest, "all through life I have awaited the fulfillment of a prophecy; and, when I read these poems, I hoped that it might be fulfilled in you."

"You hoped," answered the poet, faintly smiling, "to find in me the likeness of the Great Stone Face. And you are disappointed, as formerly with Mr. Gathergold, and Old Blood-and-Thunder, and Old Stony Phiz. Yes, Ernest, it is my doom. You must add my name to the illustrious three, and record another failure of your hopes. For--in shame and sadness I speak it, Ernest --I am not worthy to be typified by yonder kind and majestic image."

"And why?" asked Ernest. He pointed to the volume. "Are not those thoughts divine?"

"They have a strain of the Divinity," replied the poet. "You can hear in them the far-off echo of a heavenly song. But my life, dear Ernest, has not corresponded with my thought. I have had grand dreams, but they have been only dreams, because I have lived--and that, too, by my own choice-- among poor and low realities. Sometimes even--shall I dare to say it?--I lack faith in the grandeur, the beauty, and the goodness which my own works are said to have made more evident in Nature and in human life. Why, then, pure seeker of the good and true, should you hope to find in me yonder image of the divine?"

The poet spoke sadly, and his eyes were dim with tears. So, likewise, were those of Ernest.

At the hour of sunset, as had long been his frequent custom, Ernest was to talk to a gathering of the neighboring inhabitants in the open air. He and the poet, arm in arm, still talking together as they went along, proceeded to the spot. It was a small nook among the hills, with a gray precipice behind, the stern front of which was relieved by the pleasant foliage of many creeping plants that made a tapestry for the rock by hanging their vines from all its rugged angles. At a small elevation above the ground, set in a rich framework of green, there appeared a place spacious enough to admit a human figure, with freedom for movements that naturally accompany earnest thought and genuine emotion. Into this natural pulpit Ernest climbed, and looked with familiar kindness around upon his audience. They stood, or sat, or reclined upon the grass, as seemed good to each. The departing sunshine fell indirectly over them and mingled its quiet cheerfulness with the solemnity of a grove of ancient trees, beneath and amid the boughs of which the golden rays were forced to pass. In another direction was the Great Stone Face, with the same cheer, combined with the same solemnity, in its kind aspect.

Ernest began to speak, giving to the people what was in his heart and mind. His words had power because they accorded with his thoughts; and his thoughts had reality and depth because they harmonized with the life which he had always lived. It was not mere breath that this preacher uttered; they were the words of life, because a life of good deeds and holy love was melted into them. Pearls, pure and rich, had been dissolved into this precious speech. The poet, as he listened, felt that the life and character of Ernest were a nobler strain of poetry than he had ever written. His eyes glistened with tears as he gazed reverently at the noble man, and said within himself that there never was a face so worthy of a prophet and a sage as that mild, sweet, thoughtful countenance, with the glory of white hair about it. At a distance, but easily seen in the golden light of the setting sun, appeared the Great Stone Face, with white mists around it like the white hairs around the brow of Ernest. Its look of grand kindness seemed to

embrace the world.

At that moment, in sympathy with a thought which he was about to utter, Ernest's face assumed a grandeur of expression so filled with kindness that the poet, by an irresistible impulse, threw up his arms and shouted--

"Behold! Behold! Ernest is the likeness of the Great Stone Face!"

Then all the people looked, and saw that what the deep-sighted poet said was true. The prophecy was fulfilled. But Ernest, having finished what he had to say, took the poet's arm, and walked slowly homeward, still hoping that some wiser and better man than himself would by and by appear, bearing a resemblance to the Great Stone Face.

barouche — a four-wheeled carriage
buoyantly — tending to float
cavalcade — a procession
celestial — heavenly
chaotic — confused
epaulets — shoulder ornament
exterior — outside
illustrious — famous

interior — inside
pensive — thoughtful
philanthropist — a charitable person
prophecy — prediction
Providence — Divine guidance
steed — a horse
Titan — a giant
vista — a view

THINKING IT THROUGH

1. What was the prophecy of the Great Stone Face?
2. How did the Great Stone Face become a teacher to Ernest?
3. Why were the people so easily fooled each time? Why could Ernest see that each man was not the Great Stone Face in human form?
4. What did Mr. Gathergold represent? Old Blood-and-Thunder? Old Stony Phiz? The Poet?
5. Who was the "man who might have fulfilled the prophecy, and had not willed to do so?"
6. Explain this sentence: "His words had power because they accorded with his thoughts; and his thoughts had reality and depth because they harmonized with the life which he had always lived." Whom does this describe?
7. Who said, "But my life, dear Ernest, has not corresponded with my thought"? Explain the meaning of this sentence.
8. Who was the human counterpart of the Great Stone Face? Did he realize that he was the long awaited answer to the prophecy? Why?
9. Describe Ernest's character.
   How does the saying "As a man thinketh in his heart, so is he" apply to Ernest? to you? How is it the theme of the story?

ABOUT THE AUTHOR

Nathaniel Hawthorne (1804-1864), son of a Massachusetts sea captain, determined to master the new art of writing short stories. Several of his short stories and novels achieved lasting success, and he became the most outstanding New England writer of his time. His novel, The Scarlet Letter, is his most famous work.

CITIZENSHIP

— William P. Prye

This country of ours is worth our thought, our care, our labor, our lives. What a magnificent country it is! What a Republic for the people, where all are kings! Men of great wealth, of great rank, of great influence can live without difficulty under *despotic* power; but how can you and I, how can the average man endure the burden it imposes? Oh, this blessed Republic of ours stretches its hand down to men, lifts them up, while despotism puts its heavy hand on their heads and presses them down! This blessed Republic of ours speaks to every boy in the land, black or white, rich or poor, and asks him to come up higher and higher. You remember that boy out here on the prairie, the son of a widowed mother, poor, neglected perhaps by all except the dear old mother. But the Republic did not neglect him. The Republic said to that boy: "Boy, there is a ladder; its foot is on the earth, its top is in the sky. Boy, go up." And the boy mounted that ladder rung by rung; by the rung of the free schools, by the rung of the academy, by the rung of the college, by the rung of splendid service in the United States Army, by the rung of the United States House of Representatives, by the rung of the United States Senate, by the rung of the Presidency of the Great Republic, by the rung of a patient sickness and a heroic death; until James A. Garfield is a name to be forever honored in the history of our country.

Now, is not a Republic like that worth the tribute of our conscience? Is it not entitled to our best thought, to our holiest purpose?

despotic — tyrannical

THE FLAG OF OUR COUNTRY
Charles Sumner

There is the national flag. He must be cold indeed who can look upon its folds, rippling in the breeze, without pride of country. If he is in a foreign land, the flag is companionship and country itself, with all its endearments. Its highest beauty is in what it symbolizes. It is because it represents all, that all gaze at it with delight and reverence.

It is a piece of bunting lifted in the air; but it speaks sublimely, and every part has a voice. Its stripes of alternate red and white proclaim the original union of thirteen states to maintain the Declaration of Independence. Its stars of white on a field of blue proclaim that union of states constituting our national *constellation*, which receives a new star with every new state. The two together signify union past and present.

The very colors have a language which was officially recognized by our fathers. White is for purity, red for *valor*, blue for justice; and altogether, bunting, stripes, stars, and colors, blazing in the sky, make the flag of our country to be cherished by all our hearts, to be upheld by all our hands.

The Betsy Ross Flag – 1776

constellation — arrangement of stars
valor — bravery; courage